Foundation Accounting

Workbook

NVQ Accounting Units 1, 2, 3 & 4

David Cox

Michael Fardon

osborne BOOKS

Published by Osborne Books Limited
Unit 1B Everoak Estate
Bromyard Road
Worcester WR2 5HP
Tel 01905 748071
Email books@osbornebooks.co.uk
Website www.osbornebooks.co.uk

Design by Richard Holt
Cover image from Getty Images

Printed by the Bath Press, Bath

British Library Cataloguing in Publication Data
A catalogue record for this book is available from the British Library

ISBN 1 872962 52 1

Contents

workbook activities

simulations

practice examinations

appendix

About the Second Edition

The first feature that users will notice about this new edition is that it has almost doubled in size from the Year 2000 edition, providing more practice assessment material than before. The second point is that the authors have taken care to amend the assessment material so that it accurately reflects the many subtle changes brought about by the 2003 revised Standards, using the formats and terminology that students will expect to find in their Simulations and Examinations. We hope that this new text will greatly help pass rates.

Acknowledgements

The authors wish to thank the following for their help with the editing and production of the book: Mike Gilbert, Rosemarie Griffiths, Claire McCarthy and Jon Moore. Special thanks go to Roger Petheram, Series Editor, for reading, checking and advising on the development of this text. The publisher is indebted to the Association of Accounting Technicians for its generous help and advice to our authors and editors during the preparation of this text, and for permission to reproduce assessment material which has formed the basis for a number of Simulations and practice Examinations.

Authors

David Cox has more than twenty years' experience teaching accountancy students over a wide range of levels. Formerly with the Management and Professional Studies Department at Worcester College of Technology, he now lectures on a freelance basis and carries out educational consultancy work in accountancy studies. He is author and joint author of a number of textbooks in the areas of accounting, finance and banking.

Michael Fardon has extensive teaching experience of a wide range of banking, business and accountancy courses at Worcester College of Technology. He now specialises in writing business and financial texts and is General Editor at Osborne Books. He is also an educational consultant and has worked extensively in the areas of vocational business curriculum development.

How to use this book

Foundation Accounting Workbook is designed to be used alongside Osborne Books' *Foundation Accounting Tutorial* and is ideal for student use in the classroom, at home and on distance learning courses. Both the *Tutorial* and the *Workbook* are designed for students preparing for assessment for Units 1, 2, 3 and 4.

Foundation Accounting Workbook is divided into three sections: Workbook Activities, Simulations and Practice Examinations.

Workbook Activities

Workbook activities are self-contained exercises which are designed to be used to supplement the activities in the tutorial text. Many of them are more extended than the exercises in the tutorial and provide useful practice for students preparing for assessments. They have been carefully designed to reflect the style of task which students can expect to find in their assessments.

Simulations

The practice simulations in this section are designed to reflect accurately the changes brought about by the revised 2003 Standards. Simulations from the 2000 edition have been revised to cover all the performance criteria. Osborne Books is grateful to the AAT for permission to use their sample material for the remaining simulations, which have in places been slightly revised for this text, in line with the new Standards.

Practice Examinations

Osborne Books is grateful to the AAT for their kind permission to reproduce the AAT sample Examination for the new Standards and to adapt selected tasks from other Central Assessments. These practice Examination tasks have been carefully revised to reflect the changes in the new Standards.

answers

The answers to the tasks and exams in the *Workbook* are available in a separate *Tutor Pack.* Contact the Osborne Books Sales Office on 01905 748071 for details.

www.osbornebooks.co.uk

Visit the Osborne Books website, which contains Resources sections for tutors and students. These sections provide a wealth of free material, including downloadable documents and layouts and assistance with other areas of study.

Workbook activities

- This section contains activities which are suitable for use with the individual chapters of *Foundation Accounting Tutorial* from Osborne Books.
- Activities have not been included for Chapters 8,9 and 18. This is because they are supplementary 'background' chapters on the subjects of Communication and Law and are adequately covered in the Tutorial text and elsewhere in this workbook.
- Computer accounting activities for Chapters 25 to 28 are not included here because they are covered in full, both in the Tutorial text and also in the practice simulation for Unit 21 in *Office Skills* from Osborne Books.
- A number of the activities in this workbook require the completion of accounting records such as ledger accounts, daybooks and petty cash book. These three layouts may be photocopied from the Appendix (page 445). These and further examples of documents and layouts are also available as free downloads from www.osbornebooks.co.uk

1 INTRODUCTION TO ACCOUNTING

1.1 What is the difference between a sole trader, a partnership and a limited company in terms of the following factors?

- ownership of the business
- the ability to specialise in one area of the business
- liability for business debts
- the need to keep accounting records

Set out your answer in the form of a table with the above factors as headings.

1.2 Give three examples of revenue expenditure and three examples of capital expenditure.

1.3 The accounting records of Tom's sole trader business show the following account totals at the end of the year:

Capital (money invested by the owner)	£185,000
Business premises	£100,000
Bank overdraft (owed to the bank)	£80,000
Computers used in the business	£50,000
Stock held by the business	£75,000
Creditors (amounts owed by the business)	£20,000
Debtors (money owed to the business)	£60,000

(a) Sort the above accounts under the three categories set out below, and total each category:
- assets
- liabilities
- capital

(b) Insert the three totals into the accounting equation

assets minus liabilities equals capital

If the equation does not balance, check your categories in (a) above.

(c) Tom has increased the bank overdraft to buy more stock costing £10,000. Adjust the totals in the equation. It should still balance; if it does not, check your workings.

2 DOCUMENTS FOR GOODS AND SERVICES SUPPLIED

INTRODUCTION

You work as an accounts assistant at Compusupply Limited, a business which sells computer supplies such as disks and listing paper to a wide range of customers.

It is your job to process incoming orders which arrive in the form of purchase orders, faxes and telephoned orders.

You also deal with the accounting side of returned goods and you issue credit notes when credit is due.

You are also in charge of sending out statements.

You are authorised to issue invoices without reference to the accounts supervisor as long as the account is kept within its credit limit. You are required to refer any difficulties and likely excesses over credit limits to your supervisor.

Compusupply Limited normally operates a computer accounting system, but unfortunately the system has crashed and you have been asked to process all the necessary documents by hand until the hard disk has been repaired. The crash is a serious one, so you may be without the computer for over a week.

You have been given the following information:

CUSTOMER DETAILS
(EXTRACTS FROM COMPUSUPPLY FILES)

customer	**account number**	**discount %**	**credit limit £**	**balance £**
Andrews, R C	234	10	1000	750.00
Harber Employment Agency	341	10	1000	456.75
Case, Justin	209	10	1000	218.50
P C Mack Limited	197	20	5000	3190.00
Singh, I	222	10	1000	00.00
Singh, R, Retail	265	20	3500	2185.00
Townsend Litho	409	20	5000	4756.75
Zebra Designs Ltd	376	10	1000	487.50

COMPUSUPPLY CATALOGUE (EXTRACT)

code	product	unit price	£ (excl VAT)
OMHD10	OM 3.5 inch diskettes DSHD	boxes of 10	5.50
Z100	Zip 100MB cartridges	each	12.99
LP80	Computer listing paper 80 column	2000 sheet box	14.99
LP132	Computer listing paper 132 column	2000 sheet box	19.99
SQ44	Syquest disk 44MB	each	36.99
SQ88	Syquest disk 88MB	each	42.99
SQ200	Syquest disk 200MB	each	49.99
DB40	Floppy storage box (40 disks)	each	4.99
DB80	Floppy storage box (80 disks)	each	5.99
AG1	VDU anti-glare screen (mesh)	each	11.99
AG2	VDU anti-glare screen (glass)	each	19.99

ACTIVITIES

2.1 You have to check a batch of invoices to make sure the correct customer trade discount of 10% has been applied.

The totals before deduction of discount are:

(a) £67.50

(b) £45.00

(c) £107.95

(d) £12,567.95

(e) £12.75

(f) £89.00

(g) £400.00

(h) £17,450.50

(i) £1.75

(j) £30.33

You are to work out the net totals before VAT. Remember to round up or down to the nearest penny.

2.2 You have to check the VAT calculation on a further batch of invoices. The totals before VAT are:

(a) £40.00

(b) £8.00

(c) £75.00

(d) £675.50

You are to work out the VAT *and* the final total in each case. Remember to round VAT amounts down to the nearest penny in each case.

2.3 Your colleague reminds you that a settlement discount of 2.5% is due on the four invoices in the previous task. You are to adjust the VAT to allow for a settlement discount of 2.5% and recalculate the totals, but remembering that the net total shown on the invoice will *not* be reduced - only the VAT amount.

2.4 In the morning post there are three purchase orders. You are to complete invoices for all three orders. The date is 20 October 2004 and the invoices should be numbered consecutively from 309530. Blank invoices are printed on the pages that follow the purchase orders.

JUSTIN CASE ***insurance services***
2 Oakfield Business Centre
Letchfield
LT1 7TR
Tel 01903 273423

PURCHASE ORDER

TO
Compusupply Limited
Unit 17 Elgar Estate,
Broadfield, BR7 4ER

purchase order no 58345

date 17 October 2004

product code	quantity	description
LP80	2 boxes	Computer listing paper, 80 columns

Authorised signature *J Case* date *17.10.04*

R SINGH RETAIL
2 The Crescent
Broadfield
BR6 3TR
Tel 01908 456291

PURCHASE ORDER

TO
Compusupply Limited
Unit 17 Elgar Estate,
Broadfield, BR7 4ER

purchase order no 353453

date 17 October 2004

product code	quantity	description
OMHD10	10	OM 3.5 inch floppy disks

Authorised signature *R Singh* date *17.10.04*

P C Mack Ltd
57 New Road
Broadfield
BR3 6TF
Tel 01908 456291

PURCHASE ORDER

TO
Compusupply Limited
Unit 17 Elgar Estate,
Broadfield, BR7 4ER

purchase order no 14535

date 15 October 2004

product code	quantity	description
SQ44	2	Syquest 44MB disks

Authorised signature *Steve Gates* date *15.10.04*

INVOICE

COMPUSUPPLY LIMITED

Unit 17 Elgar Estate, Broadfield, BR7 4ER
Tel 01908 765756 Fax 01908 765777 Email rob@compusupply.u-net.com
VAT Reg GB 0745 4689 13

invoice to

invoice no

account

your reference

date/tax point

product code	description	quantity	price	unit	total	discount %	net

goods total	
VAT	
TOTAL	

terms
Net monthly
Carriage paid
E & OE

INVOICE

COMPUSUPPLY LIMITED

Unit 17 Elgar Estate, Broadfield, BR7 4ER
Tel 01908 765756 Fax 01908 765777 Email rob@compusupply.u-net.com
VAT Reg GB 0745 4689 13

invoice to

invoice no

account

your reference

date/tax point

product code	description	quantity	price	unit	total	discount %	net

goods total	
VAT	
TOTAL	

terms
Net monthly
Carriage paid
E & OE

INVOICE

COMPUSUPPLY LIMITED

Unit 17 Elgar Estate, Broadfield, BR7 4ER
Tel 01908 765756 Fax 01908 765777 Email rob@compusupply.u-net.com
VAT Reg GB 0745 4689 13

invoice to

invoice no

account

your reference

date/tax point

product code	description	quantity	price	unit	total	discount %	net

goods total	
VAT	
TOTAL	

terms
Net monthly
Carriage paid
E & OE

2.5 Check the invoice extracts shown below with the Catalogue and customer discount list, making sure that the details and the calculations are correct. Where there are errors, correct them in red ink.

Note: VAT is always rounded down to the nearest penny. No settlement discounts are involved.

(a) Invoice to R C Andrews

code	description	quantity	price	total	discount %	net
AG1	VDU anti-glare screen (glass)	1	19.99	19.99	20	15.99

goods total	15.99
VAT @ 17.5%	2.79
TOTAL	18.78

(b) Invoice to I Singh

code	description	quantity	price	total	discount %	net
DB40	Floppy storage box (40)	4	4.99	19.96	10	15.97
				goods total		15.97
				VAT @ 17.5%		2.79
				TOTAL		13.18

(c) Invoice to Harber Employment Agency

code	description	quantity	price	total	discount %	net
OMHD10	OM 3.5 inch disks DSHD	10 boxes	5.50	55.00	20	44.00
				goods total		44.00
				VAT @ 17.5%		7.70
				TOTAL		51.70

2.6 When you return from lunch there are two telephone messages for you:

> **telephone message**
>
> **to** *order processing*
>
> **date** *20.10.04* **time** *13.45*
>
> *Townsend Litho telephoned. They want to order ten 200MB Syquest disks as soon as possible. Can you get them off by carrier today? Thanks. Sue.*

Townsend Litho is a well-established customer with a good record of paying on time.

> **telephone message**
>
> **to** *order processing*
>
> **date** *20.10.04* **time** *13.45*
>
> *Zebra Designs called. They want a box of computer listing paper. 80 columns.*
>
> *Thanks. Hanif.*

On your return from lunch a colleague mentions that he thought he saw a notice in the local paper about Zebra Designs going 'bust'. You look in the official announcement column of the paper and see that your colleague is correct – a creditors' meeting is called for next Monday. Zebra Designs is in deep financial trouble.

You are to

(a) State what you would do in response to the two telephone messages.

(b) Describe the likely course of action taken by Compusupply in response to the two situations.

2.7 It is now a week later – 27 October 2004 – and the computer system is still not working, so you have to complete all documents by hand.

During the course of the day you receive two returns notes (printed on the next page)

You are to

(a) Write down on the R Singh Retail returns note what has gone wrong with the order.

(b) Complete the credit notes as requested (the documents are printed on the page following the returns notes).

R SINGH RETAIL
2 The Crescent
Broadfield
BR6 3TR
Tel 01908 456291

RETURNS NOTE

TO
Compusupply Limited
Unit 17 Elgar Estate,
Broadfield, BR7 4ER

returns note no 353453

date 22 October 2004

product code	quantity	description
OMHD10	9 boxes	OM 3.5 inch floppy disks

REASON FOR RETURN: too many disks sent – only 10 disks ordered. Please credit.

signature *R Singh* date 22.10.04

P C Mack Ltd
57 New Road
Broadfield
BR3 6TF
Tel 01908 456291

RETURNS NOTE

TO
Compusupply Limited
Unit 17 Elgar Estate,
Broadfield, BR7 4ER

purchase order no 14535

date 23 October 2004

product code	quantity	description
SQ44	1	Syquest 44MB data disk.

REASON FOR RETURN: faulty disk. Please credit.

signature *Steve Gates* date 23.10.04

CREDIT NOTE

COMPUSUPPLY LIMITED

Unit 17 Elgar Estate, Broadfield, BR7 4ER
Tel 01908 765756 Fax 01908 765777 Email rob@compusupply.u-net.com
VAT Reg GB 0745 4689 13

to

credit note no
account
your reference
our invoice
date/tax point

product code	description	quantity	price	unit	total	discount %	net

REASON FOR CREDIT:

goods total	
VAT	
TOTAL	

CREDIT NOTE

COMPUSUPPLY LIMITED

Unit 17 Elgar Estate, Broadfield, BR7 4ER
Tel 01908 765756 Fax 01908 765777 Email rob@compusupply.u-net.com
VAT Reg GB 0745 4689 13

to

credit note no
account
your reference
our invoice
date/tax point

product code	description	quantity	price	unit	total	discount %	net

REASON FOR CREDIT:

goods total	
VAT	
TOTAL	

2.8 It is now 31 October. The computer accounts package has been fixed and will start operating again from Monday 3 November. In the meantime you have to make out the customer statements. Using the start-of-month balances and all the transactions during the month, complete statements for R Singh Retail, P C Mack Limited and Justin Case. The statements are printed in the text.

The two payments you have received for these customers is a cheque for £218.50 from Justin Case on October 7 and a cheque for £3190.00 from P C Mack Limited on October 10.

STATEMENT

COMPUSUPPLY LIMITED

Unit 17 Elgar Estate, Broadfield, BR7 4ER
Tel 01908 765756 Fax 01908 765777 Email rob@compusupply.u-net.com
VAT Reg GB 0745 4689 13

to

account

date

date	details	debit	credit	balance

AMOUNT NOW DUE	

STATEMENT

COMPUSUPPLY LIMITED

Unit 17 Elgar Estate, Broadfield, BR7 4ER
Tel 01908 765756 Fax 01908 765777 Email rob@compusupply.u-net.com
VAT Reg GB 0745 4689 13

to

account

date

date	details	debit	credit	balance

AMOUNT NOW DUE	

STATEMENT

COMPUSUPPLY LIMITED

Unit 17 Elgar Estate, Broadfield, BR7 4ER
Tel 01908 765756 Fax 01908 765777 Email rob@compusupply.u-net.com
VAT Reg GB 0745 4689 13

to

account

date

date	details	debit	credit	balance

AMOUNT NOW DUE	

3 ACCOUNTING FOR CREDIT SALES AND SALES RETURNS

3.1 Which one of the following is a prime document?

(a) sales day book

(b) statement of account sent to T Smith, a debtor

(c) sales invoice

(d) sales account

Answer (a) or (b) or (c) or (d)

3.2 Which one of the following is entered in the sales returns day book?

(a) sales invoice

(b) pro-forma invoice

(c) statement of account sent to T Smith, a debtor

(d) credit note issued

Answer (a) or (b) or (c) or (d)

3.3 Define the following:

- prime document
- book of prime entry
- double-entry book-keeping
- account
- ledger

In the Activities which follow, the rate of Value Added Tax is to be calculated at the current rate (17.5% at the time of writing). When calculating VAT amounts, you should ignore fractions of a penny, ie round down to a whole penny.

For Activities 3.4 and 3.5 use a cross-referencing system incorporating the following:

- *sales day book – SDB 55*
  sales returns day book – SRDB 10
- *sales ledger account numbers*
  Dines Stores – account no 86
  Meadow Golf Club – account no 135
  Raven Retailers Ltd – account no 170
  Teme Sports Ltd – account no 178
  Wyvern Stores – account no 195
- *main ledger account numbers*
  sales account – account no 4001
  sales returns account – account no 4010
  Value Added Tax account– account no 2200

3.4 Pensax Products Limited manufactures plastic goods which are sold direct to shops. During November 2004 the following credit transactions took place:

2004	
3 Nov	Sold goods to Dines Stores £265 + VAT, invoice no 3592
5 Nov	Sold goods to Raven Retailers Limited, £335 + VAT, invoice no 3593
6 Nov	Sold goods to Meadow Golf Club £175 + VAT, invoice no 3594
10 Nov	Sold goods to Wyvern Stores £455 + VAT, invoice no 3595
11 Nov	Sold goods to Dines Stores £290 + VAT, invoice no 3596
13 Nov	Sold goods to Teme Sports Limited £315 + VAT, invoice no 3597
17 Nov	Sold goods to Raven Retailers Limited £1,120 + VAT, invoice no 3598
19 Nov	Sold goods to Teme Sports Limited £825 + VAT, invoice no 3599
21 Nov	Sold goods to Dines Stores £354 + VAT, invoice no 3600
24 Nov	Sold goods to Meadow Golf Club £248 + VAT, invoice no 3601
27 Nov	Sold goods to Wyvern Stores £523 + VAT, invoice no 3602
28 Nov	Sold goods to Raven Retailers Limited £187 + VAT, invoice no 3603

You are to:

(a) enter the above transactions in Pensax Products' sales day book for November 2004

(b) record the accounting entries in Pensax Products' sales ledger and main ledger

3.5 The following details are the sales returns for Pensax Products for November 2004. They are to be:

(a) entered in the sales returns day book for November 2004

(b) recorded in the sales ledger and main ledger (use the ledgers already prepared in the answer to Activity 3.4)

2004	
10 Nov	Dines Stores returns goods £55 + VAT, credit note no CN 831 is issued
14 Nov	Wyvern Stores returns goods £60 + VAT, credit note no CN 832 is issued
19 Nov	Meadow Golf Club returns goods £46 + VAT, credit note no CN 833 is issued
24 Nov	Teme Sports Limited returns goods £127 + VAT, credit note no CN 834 is issued
28 Nov	Dines Stores returns goods £87 + VAT, credit note no CN 835 is issued

3.6 John Green runs a wholesale nursery where he grows plants, shrubs and trees. These are sold on credit to garden centres, shops, and local authorities. His book-keeper records sales in an analysed sales day book including columns for total, VAT, net, plants, shrubs, trees. During April 2004 the following credit transactions took place:

2004	
2 Apr	Sold trees to Wyvern Council £550 + VAT, invoice no 2741
4 Apr	Sold plants to Mereford Garden Centre £345 + VAT, invoice no 2742
7 Apr	Sold trees £155 and shrubs £265 (both + VAT) to JJ Gardening Services, invoice no 2743
10 Apr	Sold shrubs to Mereford Garden Centre, £275 + VAT, invoice no 2744
11 Apr	Sold plants to Dines Stores £127 + VAT, invoice no 2745
15 Apr	Sold shrubs £127 and plants £352 (both + VAT) to Wyvern Council, invoice no 2746
17 Apr	Sold plants to Harford Post Office £228 + VAT, invoice no 2247
23 Apr	Sold trees to Mereford Garden Centre £175 + VAT, invoice no 2748
25 Apr	Sold plants to Bourne Supplies £155 + VAT, invoice no 2749
29 Apr	Sold trees £265 and plants £451 (both + VAT) to Mereford Garden Centre, invoice no 2750

You are to:

(a) enter the above transactions into page 76 of the *analysed* sales day book of John Green

(b) total the day book at 30 April 2004

Notes:

- folio entries are *not* required
- entries in the sales ledger and main ledger are *not* required

4 BALANCING ACCOUNTS AND CONTROL ACCOUNT FOR SALES

4.1 Balance the following accounts at 30 June 2004, bringing down the balances on 1 July:

Sales Account

Dr			Cr		
2004		£	2004		£
			1 Jun	Balance b/d	17,351
			30 Jun	Sales Day Book	3,960

Sales Returns Account

Dr			Cr		
2004		£	2004		£
1 Jun	Balance b/d	1,084			
30 Jun	Sales Returns Day Book	320			

Value Added Tax Account

Dr			Cr		
2004		£	2004		£
30 Jun	Sales Returns Day Book	56	1 Jun	Balance b/d	1,826
			30 Jun	Sales Day Book	693

N Sharma

Dr			Cr		
2004		£	2004		£
1 Jun	Balance b/d	1,495	8 Jun	Sales Returns	141
7 Jun	Sales	422			
10 Jun	Sales	384			
15 Jun	Sales	697			

Nazir & Company

Dr			Cr		
2004		£	2004		£
1 Jun	Balance b/d	863	4 Jun	Sales Returns	47
9 Jun	Sales	279	19 Jun	Sales Returns	94
18 Jun	Sales	186			

4.2 You have the following information:

	£
• opening debtor balances at start of month	12,250
• credit sales for month	7,390
• sales returns for month	450
• cash/cheques received from debtors for month	6,910

What is the figure for closing debtor balances at the end of the month?

(a) £12,280

(b) £13,180

(c) £12,220

(d) £11,320

Answer (a) or (b) or (c) or (d)

4.3 Would the following errors cause a difference between the balance of the sales ledger control account and the total of the balances in the subsidiary (sales) ledger?

(a) The sales day book was overcast (overadded) by £100.

(b) The amount of a sales invoice was debited to the account of Wyvern Traders instead of Wyvern Tiling.

(c) An invoice for £54 was recorded in the sales day book as £45.

4.4 Prepare a sales ledger control account for the month of April 2004 from the following information:

2004		£
1 Apr	Debit balance brought down	16,395
30 Apr	Credit sales for month	18,647
	Sales returns	2,804
	Cash/cheques received from debtors	21,086

Balance the account at 30 April 2004.

4.5 The main ledger of Mereford Supplies contains the following accounts on 1 November 2004:

sales	balance £24,685.39 credit
sales returns	balance £2,146.83 debit
Value Added Tax	balance £1,086.30 credit

The subsidiary (sales) ledger contains the following accounts on 1 November 2004:

Burton and Company	balance £1,472.41 debit
Haig and Sons	balance £462.28 debit
Norton Traders	balance £392.48 debit
Shipley Limited	balance £68.87 debit
Yarnold Limited	balance £976.18 debit

The following transactions, which have been authorised by the accounts supervisor, took place during November 2004:

4 Nov	Sold goods on credit to Burton and Company £542.51 + VAT, invoice no 7349
6 Nov	Sold goods on credit to Haigh and Sons £368.29 + VAT, invoice no 7350
11 Nov	Norton Traders returned goods £68.59 + VAT, credit note no CN 547 issued
14 Nov	Sold goods on credit to Yarnold Limited £241.76 + VAT, invoice no 7351
16 Nov	Sold goods on credit to Norton Traders £393.43 + VAT, invoice no 7352
17 Nov	Sold goods on credit to Shipley Limited £627.95 + VAT, invoice no 7353
20 Nov	Yarnold Limited returned goods £110.55 + VAT, credit note no CN 548 issued
24 Nov	Sold goods on credit to Burton and Company £197.52 + VAT, invoice no 7354
25 Nov	Sold goods on credit to Haigh and Sons £315.69 + VAT, invoice no 7355
29 Nov	Shipley Limited returned goods £107.46 + VAT, credit note no CN 549 issued

You are to:

(a) prepare the accounts in the main ledger – including a sales ledger control account – and subsidiary (sales) ledger of Mereford Supplies and record the balances at 1 November 2004

(b) enter the above transactions in Mereford Supplies' sales day book and sales returns day book for November 2004

(c) from the books of prime entry, record the accounting entries in the main ledger and subsidiary (sales) ledger, balancing all accounts at the month-end (30 November 2004)

(d) reconcile the control account balance with the subsidiary accounts at 1 November and 30 November 2004

5 RECEIVING AND RECORDING PAYMENTS

5.1 You are operating a cash till at the firm where you work. Today the cash float at the start of the day is £22.30, made up as follows:

2 x £5 notes	=	£10.00
6 x £1 coins	=	£6.00
6 x 50p coins	=	£3.00
8 x 20p coins	=	£1.60
10 x 10p coins	=	£1.00
8 x 5p coins	=	£0.40
12 x 2p coins	=	£0.24
6 x 1p coins	=	£0.06
		£22.30

The following are the sales which pass through the till today:

		Amount of sales £	*Notes and/or coin tendered*
Customer	1	7.50	£10 note
	2	3.38	£5 note
	3	2.29	two £1 coins and a 50p coin
	4	18.90	£20 note
	5	6.04	£10 note, £1 coin, two 2p coins
	6	26.36	three £10 notes
	7	4.30	four £1 coins and a 50p coin

You are to:

(a) state the amount of change to be given to each customer

(b) state the notes and/or coin that will be given in change, using the minimum number possible

(c) calculate the denominations of notes and coin that will remain in the till at the end of the day

(d) retain a cash float which does not exceed £30.00 (show the denominations of notes and coin); the remainder of the cash is to be banked (show denominations)

(e) prepare a summary of the day's transactions in the following form:

		£
	cash float at start	22.30
plus	sales made during the day	______
equals	amount of cash held at end of day	
less	cash float retained for next day	______
	amount banked	======

5.2 You work as an accounts assistant in the Accounts Department of Mercia Pumps Ltd, Unit 13, Severn Trading Estate, Mereford MR3 4GF. Today is 3 April 2004. In the morning's post are a number of cheques enclosed with remittance advices. These cheques are illustrated below.

Examine the cheques carefully, and identify any problems, and state what action (if any) you will take, and why. Draft letters where appropriate for your Manager's (Mrs D Strong) signature.

You note from your records that the addresses are as follows:

(a) The Accounts Department, A & S Systems, 5 High Street, Mereford MR1 2JF

(b) Mrs P Thorne, Hillside Cottage, Mintfield, MR4 9HG

(c) The Accounts Department, C Darwin Ltd, 89 Baker Street, Mereford MR2 6RG

(d) Mr I M King, 56 Beaconsfield Drive, Pershore MR7 5GF

(a)

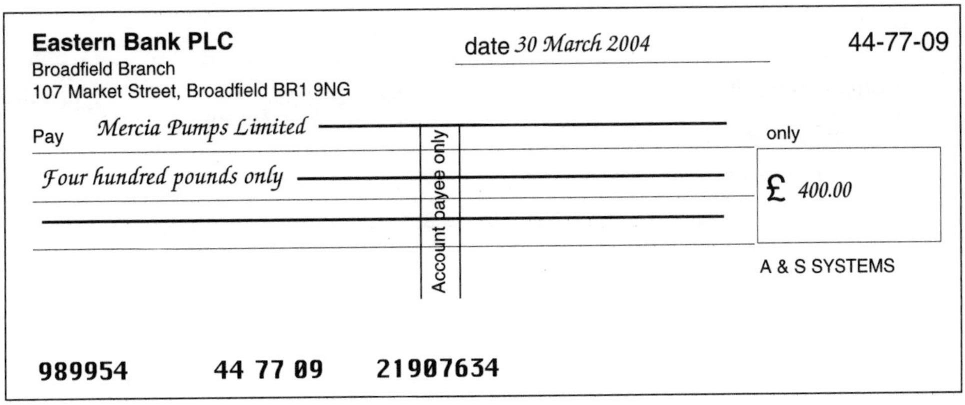
Eastern Bank PLC
Broadfield Branch
107 Market Street, Broadfield BR1 9NG
date *30 March 2004*
44-77-09
Pay *Mercia Pumps Limited*
only
Four hundred pounds only
Account payee only
£ *400.00*
A & S SYSTEMS
989954 44 77 09 21907634

(b)

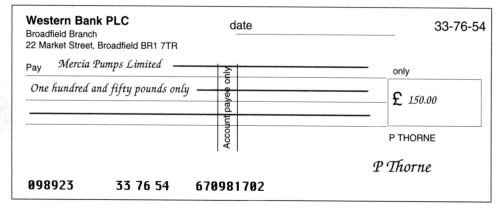

Western Bank PLC
Broadfield Branch
22 Market Street, Broadfield BR1 7TR

date

33-76-54

Pay *Mercia Pumps Limited*

One hundred and fifty pounds only

Account payee only

only

£ *150.00*

P THORNE

P Thorne

098923 33 76 54 670981702

(c)

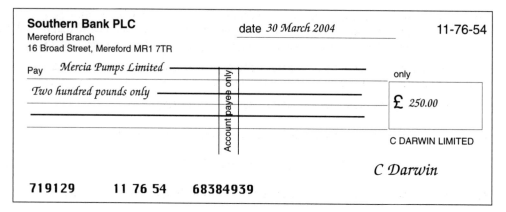

Southern Bank PLC
Mereford Branch
16 Broad Street, Mereford MR1 7TR

date *30 March 2004*

11-76-54

Pay *Mercia Pumps Limited*

Two hundred pounds only

Account payee only

only

£ *250.00*

C DARWIN LIMITED

C Darwin

719129 11 76 54 68384939

(d)

Mr King has made the cheque payable to your Sales Director, John Hopkins.

Northern Bank PLC
Mereford Branch
28 High Street, Mereford MR1 8FD

date *30 March 2004*

22-01-59

Pay *John Hopkins*

Sixty pounds only

Account payee only

only

£ *60.00*

I KING

I M King

123456 22 01 59 37537147

5.3 You work as a cashier at Cripplegate DIY store. The date today is January 20 2004. You deal with a number of customers who wish to make payment using cheques and cheque card. What action would you take in the following circumstances, and why?

(a) Card limit £100, expiry June 2004, code 11-76-54. The name on the card is J E Drew. The lady explains that she has just got married, and Drew is her maiden name.

Southern Bank PLC
Mereford Branch
16 Broad Street, Mereford MR1 7TR

date *20 January 2004* 11-76-54

Pay *Cripplegate DIY* only

Ninety pounds only £ *90.00*

Account payee only

J E DREW

J E Jones

979782 11 76 54 27289931

(b) Card limit £100, expiry May 2004, code 22-01-59. Mr King wants to buy some garden furniture costing £150.95. He has made out the following cheques in advance.

Northern Bank PLC
Mereford Branch
28 High Street, Mereford MR1 8FD

date *20 January 2004* 22-01-59

Pay *Cripplegate DIY* only

One hundred pounds only £ *100.00*

Account payee only

I KING

I M King

122874 22 01 59 37537147

Northern Bank PLC
Mereford Branch
28 High Street, Mereford MR1 8FD

date *20 January 2004* 22-01-59

Pay *Cripplegate DIY* only

Fifty pounds 95p only £ *50.95*

Account payee only

I KING

I M King

122875 22 01 59 37537147

(c) Card limit £200, expiry April 2004, code 33-76-54. The cheque card is handed to you in a plastic wallet and the signature on the card does not quite tally with the signature on the cheque. The customer says that he has sprained his wrist and this has affected his writing.

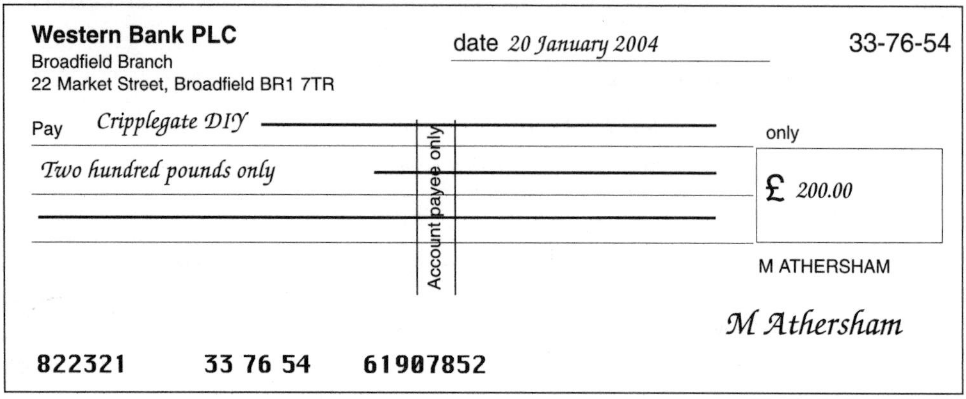

Western Bank PLC
Broadfield Branch
22 Market Street, Broadfield BR1 7TR

date *20 January 2004*

33-76-54

Pay *Cripplegate DIY*

Two hundred pounds only

Account payee only

only

£ *200.00*

M ATHERSHAM

M Athersham

822321 33 76 54 61907852

(d) Card limit £200, expiry August 2004, code 88-76-54. Mrs Blackstone is in a great hurry and asks you to be as quick as you can. She seems to be rather agitated. The signature on the cheque matches the signature on the card and everything else seems to be in order.

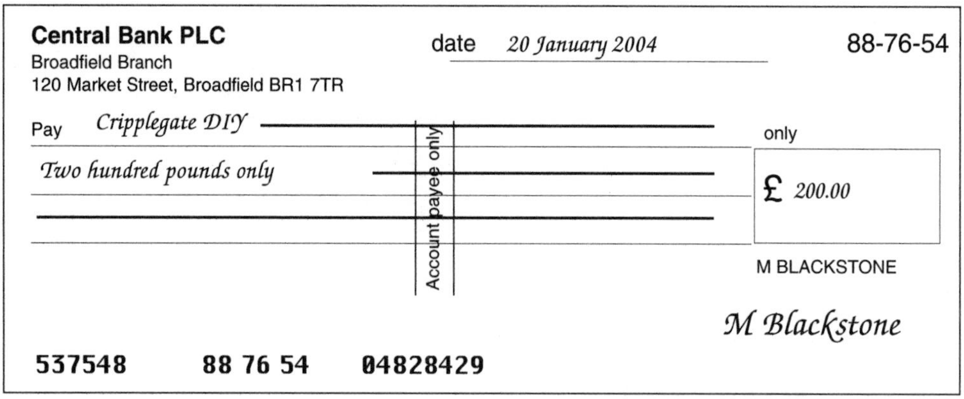

Central Bank PLC
Broadfield Branch
120 Market Street, Broadfield BR1 7TR

date *20 January 2004*

88-76-54

Pay *Cripplegate DIY*

Two hundred pounds only

Account payee only

only

£ *200.00*

M BLACKSTONE

M Blackstone

537548 88 76 54 04828429

6 PAYING INTO THE BANK

6.1 You are working in the accounts department of Martley Fruits Limited, Maytree Farm, Martley MR7 2LX. Part of your job is to deal with the cheques received in the post, and to prepare those cheques for banking. During the course of a working day you deal with a number of cheques, some of which may cause problems. Your supervisor, Mark Tucker, asks you to identify the problems, and state in each case how you would deal with them. Write down your answers using the schedule on the next page.

	customer	*amount*	*comments*
(a)	Henry Young & Co	£1,245	you need to find out whether this cheque is to be paid before you can despatch the goods – rapid clearance is required
(b)	Ivor Longway	£342.90	the date on the cheque is three months old
(c)	Ned Morgan	£837.89	the date on the cheque is ten months old
(d)	Lisa Jones	£90.00	you receive this cheque from the bank; the cheque is marked 'Post dated'; on inspecting the cheque you see that the cheque is dated three months in the future
(e)	N Patel	£78.00	you receive this cheque from the bank; it is marked 'Payment Countermanded by order of Drawer'
(f)	N Trebbiano	£78.98	there is no crossing on the cheque

When you have checked your answer schedule with your tutor you are to draft appropriate letters for your supervisor's signature to the following customers (use today's date):

J Maxwell Ltd, 67 The Circus, Bradstreet, BD5 8GY

Ned Morgan, 72 Malvern Crescent, Milton Park, MR6 2CS

Lisa Jones, c/o The Kings Arms, Leatherton, MR6 9SD

customer	problem	solution
Henry Young & Co		
Ivor Longway		
Ned Morgan		
Lisa Jones		
N Patel		
N Trebbiano		

6.2 A colleague, Lisa, who works in the Accounts Department of Wyvern (Office Products) Limited has been handed the latest bank statement by your supervisor, Alfred Hunter. Lisa, who is new to the job, has two queries:

- a credit on 2 April appears as £485.02; your paying slip copy shows the total as £485.04.
- Lisa says she cannot find a paying-in slip copy for the £1,500 received on 4 April

The documentation you have available is shown below.

NATIONAL BANK PLC **Statement of Account**

Branch: Mereford

Account: Wyvern (Office Products) Ltd

Account no 01099124 Sheet no 105 Statement date 10 Apr 2003

Date	Details	Withdrawals	Deposits	Balance
2003		£	£	£
1 Apr	Balance brought forward			1,300.00 Cr
1 Apr	Credit		2,000.00	3,300.00 Cr
1 Apr	BACS Prime Hotels Ltd		2,000.00	5,300.00 Cr
2 Apr	Credit		485.02	5,785.02 Cr
3 Apr	Bank charges	70.00		5,715.02 Cr
4 Apr	NationalNet webshop sales		1,500.00	7,215.02 Cr
10 Apr	Cheque 123745	1,860.00		5,355.02 Cr

Date 2.4.03

Credit Wyvern (OP) Ltd

£50 notes		
£20 notes	40	00
£10 notes	50	00
£5 notes	25	00
£1/ £2	4	00
50p	1	50
20p		80
10p,5p		25
Bronze		17
Total Cash	121	72
Cheques etc	363	32
£	485	04

Date 2.4.03 **bank giro credit**

Cashier's stamp and initials

National Bank
Mereford

Credit: Wyvern (Office Products) Limited

Code: 60-24-48 Account: 01099124

Number of cheques 3

Paid in by T. Newnandy

Do not write below this line

£50 notes		
£20 notes	40	00
£10 notes	50	00
£5 notes	25	00
£1/ £2	4	00
50p	1	50
20p		80
10p,5p		25
Bronze		17
Total Cash	121	72
Cheques etc	363	32
£	485	04

60-24-48 01099124 77

Counterfoil			Cheques		
	158	97	CAMTEC LTD	158	97
	104	35	BRUSON & CO	104	35
	100	00	J LEWIS	100	00
£	363	32	Carried over £	363	32

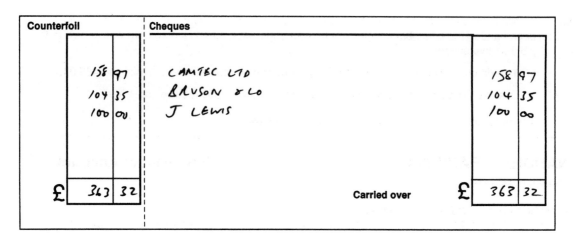

REMITTANCE ADVICE

BRUSON & CO

25 Melody Chambers, Gloucester GL1 2RF

Tel 01452 37232182 Fax 01452 37234496

Wyvern (Office Products) Ltd
12 Lower Hyde Street
Mereford MR1 2JF

Cheque No	774474
Date	18 February 2003
Account	2947

date	our ref.	your ref.	amount	discount	payment
16.3.03	8274	35357	104.33	00.00	104.33

cheque value £ 104.33

NATIONALNET WEBSHOP SALES – PAYMENT ADVICE

Customer	Wyvern (Office Products) Ltd
Item	Website Sales to 1 April
Amount	£1,500.00
Payment	BACS payment to account 01099124 at 60 24 48 on 4 April 2003

You are to

(a) Explain to Lisa what has happened in relation to the paying-in slip dated 1 April and the bank statement.

(b) Write down in numbered points what actions you think should be taken as a result of the mistake on the credit.

(c) Explain to Lisa what the bank statement entry on 4 April represents.

7 CASH BOOK – RECORDING RECEIPTS

7.1 The discount allowed column of the cash book is totalled at regular intervals and transferred to:

(a) the credit side of discount allowed account

(b) the debit side of discount allowed account

(c) the debit side of sales account

(d) the credit side of sales account

Answer (a) or (b) or (c) or (d)

7.2 The VAT column on the receipts side of the cash book is totalled at regular intervals and transferred to:

(a) the debit side of sales returns account

(b) the debit side of VAT account

(c) the credit side of sales account

(d) the credit side of VAT account

Answer (a) or (b) or (c) or (d)

7.3 The following are the receipts transactions of Marcle Enterprises for October 2004:

1 Oct	Balances from previous month: cash £280, bank £2,240
4 Oct	Received a cheque from a debtor, M Perry Limited, £475
5 Oct	Cash sales of £240 + VAT, received in cash
11 Oct	Received a BACS advice for £1,295 from T Francis Limited in full settlement of their account of £1,305
15 Oct	Cash sales of £320 + VAT, received in cash
17 Oct	Received a cheque for £640 from H Watson, in full settlement of her account of £660
18 Oct	Received a loan of £1,000 from the bank (no VAT)
22 Oct	Cash sales of £480 + VAT, received half in cash, and half by cheque
24 Oct	Rent received from tenant, £150 in cash (no VAT)
30 Oct	Received a cheque for £464 from M Perry Limited in full settlement of their account of £480

The rate of Value Added Tax is 17.5%

All cheques are banked on the day of receipt

Account numbers are to be used – see next page

You are to:

- Enter the above receipts on page 67 of the three column cash book of Marcle Enterprises.
- Sub-total the money columns at 31 October.
- Show the entries to be made in the following accounts:

  subsidiary (sales) ledger
  T Francis Limited (account no 445)
  M Perry Limited (account no 675)
  H Watson (account no 840)
  main ledger
  sales ledger control account (account no 6001)
  discount allowed account (account no 6501)
  bank loan (account no 2210)
  rent received account (account no 4951)
  sales account (account no 4001)
  VAT account (account no 2200)

7.4 The following are the receipts transactions of Kendrick and Company for November 2004:

1 Nov	Balances from previous month: cash £125, bank £1,529
5 Nov	D McNamara, a debtor, settles an invoice for £100, paying £95 in cash and receiving £5 discount for prompt settlement
7 Nov	Cash sales £235 (including Value Added Tax), received by cheque
12 Nov	Rent received from tenant, £200 by cheque (no VAT)
15 Nov	Cash sales of £423 (including Value Added Tax), received by cheque
19 Nov	Received a cheque for £595 from Johnson & Co, a debtor, in full settlement of their account of £610
20 Nov	Cash sales of £94 (including Value Added Tax), received in cash
26 Nov	Received a cheque for £475 from Mendez Limited, in full settlement of their account of £500
28 Nov	Additional capital paid in, £2,500 by cheque (no VAT)

The rate of Value Added Tax is 17.5%
All cheques are banked on the day of receipt
Account numbers are to be used – see next page

You are to:

- Enter the above receipts on page 24 of the cash book of Kendrick and Company, using columns for date, details, folio, discount allowed, VAT, cash and bank.
- Sub-total the money columns at 30 November.
- Show the entries to be made in the following accounts:

subsidiary (sales) ledger

Johnson & Co (account no 355)

D McNamara (account no 460)

Mendez Limited (account no 505)

main ledger

capital account (account no 3005)

sales ledger control account (account no 6001)

discount allowed account (account no 6501)

rent received account (account no 4951)

sales account (account no 4001)

VAT account (account no 2200)

7.5 Martin Peters runs a building supplies company. He buys in bulk from manufacturers and sells in smaller quantities to trade customers on credit and to the public on cash terms. His business is registered for VAT.

He uses a cash book which analyses receipts between:

- discount allowed
- VAT
- cash sales
- subsidiary (sales) ledger
- rent received

The following transactions take place during the week commencing 19 November 2004:

19 Nov	Balances from previous week: cash £384.21, bank £2,576.80
19 Nov	Cash sales of £354.25 (including VAT), cheques received
20 Nov	Received a BACS advice for £678.11 from Barbourne Builders in full settlement of their account of £695.50
20 Nov	Cash sales of £254.88 (including VAT), cash received
21 Nov	Rent received from a tenant of part of the premises, £285.75 by cheque (no VAT)
21 Nov	Cash sales of £476.29 (including VAT), cheques received
22 Nov	Rent received from another tenant, £325.00 in cash (no VAT)
22 Nov	Cash sales of £351.48 (including VAT), cash received
23 Nov	A debtor, J Johnson, settles an invoice for £398.01, paying £389.51 by BACS, £8.50 discount being allowed for prompt settlement
23 Nov	Cash sales of £487.29 (including VAT), cheques received
23 Nov	A debtor, Wyvern Council settles an invoice for £269.24 by cheque

The rate of Value Added Tax is 17.5%

All cheques are banked on the day of receipt

Account numbers are to be used as follows:

Main ledger account codes (extract):	
1000	Cash book
2000	Sales ledger control
3000	Discount allowed
4000	Sales
5000	Rent received
6000	VAT

Subsidiary (sales) ledger account codes (extract):	
110	Barbourne Builders
440	J Johnson
930	Wyvern Council

Using the layouts on the next three pages, you are to:

- Enter the above receipts on page 45 of the analysed cash book of Martin Peters (VAT amounts should be rounded down to the nearest penny).
- Total the money columns at 23 November.
- Show the entries to be made in the main ledger and the subsidiary (sales) ledger.

ACCOUNT NO 1000 CASH BOOK (RECEIPTS)

CBR 45

Date 2004	Details	Reference	Cash £	Bank £	Discount allowed £	VAT £	Cash sales £	Subsidiary (sales) ledger £	Rent received £	Subsidiary (sales) ledger code
	Main ledger codes	DR								
		CR								

MAIN LEDGER

2000 Sales Ledger Control							
Date	Details	Folio	Amount	Date	Details	Folio	Amount
2004			£	2004			£

3000 Discount Allowed							
Date	Details	Folio	Amount	Date	Details	Folio	Amount
2004			£	2004			£

4000 Sales							
Date	Details	Folio	Amount	Date	Details	Folio	Amount
2004			£	2004			£

5000 Rent Received							
Date	Details	Folio	Amount	Date	Details	Folio	Amount
2004			£	2004			£

MAIN LEDGER

6000 VAT							
Date	Details	Folio	Amount	Date	Details	Folio	Amount
2004			£	2004			£

SUBSIDIARY (SALES) LEDGER

110 Barbourne Builders							
Date	Details	Folio	Amount	Date	Details	Folio	Amount
2004			£	2004			£

440 J Johnson							
Date	Details	Folio	Amount	Date	Details	Folio	Amount
2004			£	2004			£

930 Wyvern Council							
Date	Details	Folio	Amount	Date	Details	Folio	Amount
2004			£	2004			£

10 DOCUMENTS FOR GOODS AND SERVICES RECEIVED

10.1 You have just started work as an accounts assistant in the purchasing department of Litho Printers. Your supervisor has asked you to buy 150 reams (a ream is 500 sheets) of standard quality white A4 copy paper. He said "shop around if you can – prices can vary a lot."

You have telephoned four different stationery suppliers for their stationery catalogues and have made enquiries about special offers on copy paper. The best deals seem to be from Saxon Supplies. An extract from their catalogue (which they have faxed through) is shown below.

SAXON SUPPLIES

Unit 12 Hereward Industrial Estate, Warborough, WA3 5TG

Tel 01807 282482 Fax 01807 282412 Email JJ@Saxon.u-net-com.uk

BARGAINS OF THE MONTH!

reference	*product*	*unit*	*list price (VAT excl)*	*sale price (VAT excl)*
RCA4	A4 Roxo 80gsm copy paper (white only) standard quality	ream	3.49	2.79
REFA4	A4 Roxo 80gsm copy paper (white – extra fine quality)	ream	4.99	3.49
RLA4	A4 Roxo 80gsm laser paper	ream	5.49	4.99
CCA4	Colour 80gsm copy paper Add code to your order ref: R (red) B (blue) Y (yellow)	ream	5.50	4.50
EWDLP	White self-seal DL envelopes (plain)	1000 box	25.00	10.99
EWDLSS	White self-seal DL envelopes (window)	1000 box	35.00	16.99
N1	'Nifty' air bubble mail envelopes 200mm x 300mm	100 box	22.00	18.00
N2	'Nifty' air bubble mail envelopes 235mm x 370mm	100 box	25.00	21.00
FR15	Fax roll 210mm x 15m	roll	2.85	1.50
FR30	Fax roll 216mm x 30m	roll	5.00	3.50

Your supervisor, who has seen the Saxon Supplies prices, says that she also wants to order 50 fax rolls (30m) and 5 boxes of white self-seal DL window envelopes which are used to send out customer statements.

You are to complete the purchase order shown below for the 150 reams of ordinary white copy paper and the extra items requested by the supervisor. You are authorised to sign the order (use your own name). Saxon Supplies has said over the telephone that you can have an initial 15% discount on all orders. The purchase order number is 2892. The date is 8 December 2004.

PURCHASE ORDER

litho printers

Unit 7 Buttermere Estate
Station Road
Broadfield
BR6 3TR
Tel 01908 456291 Fax 01908 456913

to

purchase order no

date

product code	quantity	description

Authorised signature..date..................................

10.2 Later in the morning you have to check a delivery note for goods just received against the original purchase order (see page 46). Write a letter to the supplier (see page 47) explaining what is wrong with the delivery. Use your own name and the title 'Accounts Assistant'. The date is 8 December 2004.

PURCHASE ORDER

litho printers

Unit 7 Buttermere Estate
Station Road
Broadfield
BR6 3TR
Tel 01908 456291 Fax 01908 456913

to

Eleco Supplies
79 Broadacre
Boreham
BO7 6TG

purchase order no 3601

date 20 November 2004

product code	quantity	description
23477C	5	Typo office chairs, charcoal

Authorised signature *A Morello* date *20.11.04*

DELIVERY NOTE

eleco supplies

79 Broadacre
Boreham
BO7 6TG
Tel 01208 070111 Fax 01208 070149

to

Litho Printers Limited
Unit 7 Buttermere Estate
Station Road
Broadfield
BR6 3TR

Delivery Note No 39823
Purchase Order no 3601
Date 5 December 2004
Delivery Lightning Carriers

product code	quantity	description
22477C	5	Executive chairs, charcoal

Received in good condition

signature *R Smithers* date *8.12.04*

litho printers

Unit 7 Buttermere Estate, Station Road,
Broadfield BR6 3TR
Tel 01908 456291 Fax 01908 456913
E-mail ben@litho.u-net.com

Litho Printers Limited. Registered office: Unit 7 Buttermere Estate, Station Road, Broadfield BR6 3TR
Registered in England No 3539857. VAT Reg GB 32 73687 78

10.3 After lunch on the same day (8 December 2004) you have to check three incoming invoices against the appropriate goods received notes which have been raised (see pages 48 to 50). They should be checked for accuracy and to make sure that they apply to the goods supplied. You are to make a list of any errors or discrepancies and pass it to your supervisor on the schedule on page 51. Each of the suppliers normally gives 20% trade discount, but no cash discount.

INVOICE

JUMBO STATIONERY

91 HIGH STREET, BROADFIELD, BR7 4ER
Tel 01908 129426 Fax 01908 129919

invoice to

Litho Printers Limited
Unit 7 Buttermere Estate
Station Road
Broadfield BR6 3TR

invoice no 234672
account 2984
your reference 3627
date/tax point 1 December 2004

product code	description	quantity	price	unit	total	discount %	net
JB234	Jetstream Biros, finepoint, black	20	2.25	box	45.00	10	40.50

terms
Net monthly
Carriage paid
E & OE

goods total	40.50
VAT	7.08
TOTAL	47.58

JAVELIN OFFICE MACHINES

invoice

Unit 19 Elgar Estate, Broadfield, BR7 4ER
Tel 01908 765101 Fax 01908 765304

invoice to

Litho Printers Limited
Unit 7 Buttermere Estate
Station Road
Broadfield BR6 3TR

invoice no 10483
account 935
order reference 3629
date/tax point 2 December 2004

product code	description	quantity	price	unit	total	discount %	net
M17C	Multipoint 17" colour monitor	1	499.00	item	499.00	20	399.20

terms
Net monthly
Carriage paid
E & OE

goods total	399.20
VAT	69.86
TOTAL	469.06

EDWARD HUGHES LIMITED **invoice**

Unit 3 Bronglais Estate, Pwllmadoc, LL1 4ER
Tel 01708 323242 Fax 01708 323242 VAT Reg GB 5019 46 2

invoice to

Litho Printers Limited
Unit 7 Buttermere Estate
Station Road
Broadfield BR6 3TR

invoice no	12931
account	9742
your reference	3628
date/tax point	2 December 2004

product code	description	quantity	price	unit	total	discount %	net
3883	Automatic offset crimper	1	8295.00	unit	8295.00	20	6636.00

terms
Net monthly
Carriage paid
E & OE

goods total	6636.00
VAT	1116.30
TOTAL	7752.30

litho printers

GOODS RECEIVED NOTE

GRN no. 301
supplier Jumbo Stationery
date 3 December 2004

order ref.	quantity	description
3627	15 boxes	Jetstream biros (fine point, black)

received by R Nixon .... checked by I Singh ....

condition of goods
good 15 boxes
damages
shortages 5 boxes

litho printers **GOODS RECEIVED NOTE**

GRN no. 303
supplier Javelin Office Machines
date 4 December 2004

order ref.	quantity	description
3629	1	Multipoint 17 inch colour monitor

received by J Kennedy **checked by** I Singh

condition of goods good √
damages
shortages

litho printers **GOODS RECEIVED NOTE**

GRN no. 302
supplier Edward Hughes Ltd
date 4 December 2004

order ref.	quantity	description
3628	1	Automatic offset crimper

received by J Kennedy **checked by** M Jones

condition of goods good √
damages
shortages

date	Order no.	Action to be taken

10.4 Today it is 12 December 2004 and the stationery order from Saxon Supplies (see Task 10.1) has arrived. The goods received note shows that the correct quantity of goods has been received and that there are no wrong goods or damaged items.

You have now been passed the invoice for checking against the original order (produced in Task 10.1). If there are any problems with the invoice, write them down on the memorandum on the next page. Address the memo to your supervisor, James Ridelle. Use your own name. Your title is Accounts Assistant.

INVOICE

SAXON SUPPLIES

Unit 12 Hereward Industrial Estate, Warborough, WA3 5TG
Tel 01807 282482 Fax 01807 282412 Email JJ@Saxon.u-net-com.uk

invoice to

Litho Printers Limited
Unit 7 Buttermere Estate
Station Road
Broadfield BR6 3TR

invoice no	89422
account	230
your reference	2892
date/tax point	10 December 2004

product code	description	quantity	price	unit	total	discount %	net
RCA4	A4 Roxo 80gsm copy paper	150	3.49	ream	523.50	15	444.98
FR30	Fax roll 216mm x 30mm	50	3.50	unit	175.00	15	148.75
EWDLSS	White self-seal window DL envelopes	5	16.99	box	84.95	15	72.21

terms
Net monthly
Carriage paid
E & OE

goods total	665.94
VAT	116.53
TOTAL	782.47

MEMORANDUM

date
to
from
subject

10.5 You work for H Patel & Co, a wholesaler. You are an accounts assistant and one of your tasks is to process payments to suppliers. The business normally pays on the 7th and 21st day of each month (or the next working day). The company takes full advantage of the credit terms offered by its suppliers.

H Patel & Co has recently been having problems with its supplier ABC Import Agency, which supplies on 30 day terms. Orders have been delivered late and wrong goods have been supplied. As a result H Patel & Co withheld the August payment until a credit note for £470.00 was received in respect of wrong goods supplied.

The credit note finally arrived on 25 September 2003.

It is 7 October and you have been told that you can now process a payment to ABC Import Agency. The statement is shown below.

You are to calculate the amount owing and complete the remittance advice and cheque shown on the next page. You will not sign the cheque, as it has to be authorised and signed by Hitten Patel.

STATEMENT OF ACCOUNT

ABC Import Agency
30 Eastway Road
Manchester
M1 2RB
Tel 01601 764098 Fax 01601 764083 Email mail@abcimportco.com
VAT Reg GB 0748 4872 23

TO

H Patel & Co
76 Dockside Road
Deeford
DE1 8AS

account 3945

date 30 September 2003

date	details	debit £	credit £	balance £
2003				
1 Sep	Balance b/f			5,600.00
3 Sep	Invoice 13621	1,400.00		7,000.00
12 Sep	Invoice 13688	1,665.00		8,665.00
22 Sep	Invoice 13721	2,991.00		11,656.00
25 Sep	Credit note 744		470.00	11,186.00

TOTAL **£** 11,186.00

REMITTANCE ADVICE

TO

FROM

H Patel & Co
76 Dockside Road
Deeford
DE1 8AS
Tel 01324 8752946 Fax 01324 8752955
VAT REG GB 0745 8383 77

Account: **Date:**

date	your reference	our reference	payment amount

CHEQUE TOTAL

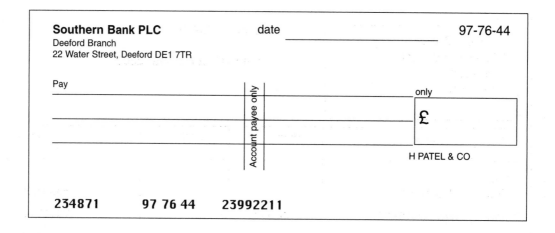

Southern Bank PLC
Deeford Branch
22 Water Street, Deeford DE1 7TR

date

97-76-44

Pay

Account payee only

only

£

H PATEL & CO

234871 97 76 44 23992211

11 ACCOUNTING FOR CREDIT PURCHASES AND PURCHASES RETURNS

11.1 Which one shows the correct accounting entries to record the purchase of goods for resale on credit?

	Debit	***Credit***
(a)	purchases returns account	supplier's account
(b)	purchases account	supplier's account
(c)	supplier's account	purchases returns account
(d)	supplier's account	purchases account

Answer (a) or (b) or (c) or (d)

In the Activities which follow, the rate of Value Added Tax is to be calculated at the current rate (17.5% at the time of writing). When calculating VAT amounts, you should ignore fractions of a penny, ie round down to a whole penny.

For Activities 11.2 and 11.3 use a cross-referencing system incorporating the following:

purchases day book – *PDB 36*

purchases returns day book – *PRDB 11*

purchases ledger account numbers

S Burston – *account no 530*

Iley Wholesalers – *account no 605*

Malvern Manufacturing – *account no 625*

SG Enterprises – *account no 720*

main ledger accounts

purchases account – *account no 5001*

purchases returns account – *account no 5010*

Value Added Tax account – *account no 2200*

11.2 During July 2004, Tyax Trading Company had the following credit transactions:

2004	
3 Jul	Bought goods from Malvern Manufacturing £170 + VAT, invoice no 7321
9 Jul	Bought goods from S Burston £265 + VAT, invoice SB745
12 Jul	Bought goods from Iley Wholesalers £450 + VAT, invoice no 4721
18 Jul	Bought goods from SG Enterprises £825 + VAT, invoice no 3947
23 Jul	Bought goods from S Burston £427 + VAT, invoice no SB773
30 Jul	Bought goods from Malvern Manufacturing £364 + VAT, invoice no 7408

You are to:

(a) enter the above transactions in Tyax Trading Company's purchases day book for July 2004

(b) record the accounting entries in Tyax Trading Company's purchases ledger and main ledger

11.3 The following are the purchases returns of Tyax Trading Company for July 2004. They are to be:

(a) entered in the purchases returns day book for July 2004

(b) recorded in the purchases ledger and main ledger (use the ledgers already prepared in the answer to Activity 11.2).

2004	
11 Jul	Returned goods to Malvern Manufacturing £70 + VAT, credit note no CN345 received
17 Jul	Returned goods to Iley Wholesalers for £85 + VAT, credit note no CN241 received
24 Jul	Returned goods to SG Enterprises for £25 + VAT, credit note no 85 received
31 Jul	Returned goods to S Burston for £55 + VAT, credit note no 295 received

11.4 The Oasis Trading Company records its credit purchases in an analysed day book with the following headings: VAT, net, goods for resale, printing, telephone. The transactions for March 2004 are as follows:

2004	
3 Mar	Bought goods for resale from Severn Valley Traders £255.50 + VAT
4 Mar	Bought goods for resale from Mercian Suppliers £356.25 + VAT
6 Mar	Received an invoice for £136.95 + VAT from Print Services Limited for printing
10 Mar	Bought goods for resale from D James Limited £368.21 + VAT
14 Mar	Received an invoice for £218.25 + VAT from United Telecom for telephone costs

17 Mar	Bought goods for resale from Wyvern Traders £45.40 + VAT
19 Mar	Bought goods for resale from A-Z Traders £496.84 + VAT
21 Mar	Received an invoice for £154.65 + VAT from Saturn Communications for telephone costs
24 Mar	Bought goods for resale from A J Knowles £151.20 + VAT
25 Mar	Bought goods for resale from Severn Valley Traders £357.24 + VAT
28 Mar	Received an invoice for £121.47 + VAT from Total Communications plc for telephone costs
31 Mar	Received an invoice for £117.25 from Print Services Limited for printing

You are to:

(a) give each invoice a unique number – starting with number 4592

(b) enter the above transactions into page 45 of the company's analysed purchases day book

(c) total the day book at 31 March 2004

Note: Entries in the purchases ledger and main ledger are not required.

12 BALANCING ACCOUNTS AND CONTROL ACCOUNT FOR PURCHASES

12.1 Balance the following accounts at 30 April 2004, bringing down the balance on 1 May:

Dr **Purchases Account** Cr

2004		£	2004		£
1 Apr	Balance b/d	33,649			
30 Apr	Purchases Day Book	7,840			

Dr **Purchases Returns Account** Cr

2004		£	2004		£
			1 Apr	Balance b/d	856
			30 Apr	Purchases Returns Day Book	400

Dr **Value Added Tax Account** Cr

2004		£	2004		£
30 Apr	Purchases Day Book	1,372	1 Apr	Balance b/d	1,873
			30 Apr	Purchases Returns Day Book	70

Dr **Shah and Company** Cr

2004		£	2004		£
23 Apr	Purchases Returns	94	1 Apr	Balance b/d	591
			9 Apr	Purchases	783
			22 Apr	Purchases	396
			28 Apr	Purchases	421

Dr **Martinez Limited** Cr

2004		£	2004		£
9 Apr	Purchases Returns	47	1 Apr	Balance b/d	965
17 Apr	Purchases Returns	141	4 Apr	Purchases	187
			20 Apr	Purchases	246
			27 Apr	Purchases	397

12.2 You have the following information:

	£
• opening creditor balances at start of month	24,795
• credit purchases for month	15,355
• purchases returns for month	420
• cash/cheques paid to creditors for month	14,935

What is the figure for closing creditor balances at the end of the month?

(a) £15,915

(b) £25,635

(c) £24,795

(d) £23,955

Answer (a) or (b) or (c) or (d)

12.3 Prepare a purchases ledger control account for the month of June 2004 from the following information:

2004		£
1 Jun	Credit balance brought down	27,932
30 Jun	Credit purchases for month	19,354
	Purchases returns	1,083
	Cash/cheques paid to creditors	22,649
	Transfer of credit balances to sales ledger	1,378

The creditors figure at 30 June is to be entered as the balancing figure.

12.4 The main ledger of Pembridge and Company contains the following accounts on 1 August 2004:

purchases	balance £16,241.38 debit
purchases returns	balance £1,854.29 credit
Value Added Tax	balance £1,437.94 credit

The subsidiary (purchases) ledger contains the following accounts on 1 August 2004:

Bakewell Limited	balance £476.81 credit
Edge and Company	balance £1,107.52 credit
M Lister	balance £908.04 credit
Percival and Company	balance £250.49 credit
Trent Supplies	balance £749.25 credit
Vector Metals Limited	balance £397.64 credit

The following transactions, which have been authorised by the accounts supervisor, took place during August 2004 (note that Pembridge and Company gives each invoice and credit note received its own unique number):

2 Aug	Bought goods on credit from Trent Supplies £179.21 + VAT, invoice no 3954
5 Aug	Bought goods on credit from Percival and Company £352.47 + VAT, invoice no 3955
6 Aug	Returned goods to Bakewell Limited £74.38 + VAT, credit note no 768
9 Aug	Bought goods on credit from M Lister £450.68 + VAT, invoice no 3956
12 Aug	Bought goods on credit from Vector Metals Limited £370.27 + VAT, invoice no 3957
14 Aug	Bought goods on credit from Edge and Company £210.48 + VAT, invoice no 3958
17 Aug	Returned goods to Percival and Company £114.36 + VAT, credit note no 769
19 Aug	Bought goods on credit from Trent Supplies £780.36 + VAT, invoice no 3959
25 Aug	Bought goods on credit from M Lister £246.33 + VAT, invoice no 3960
27 Aug	Returned goods to Vector Metals Limited £68.41 + VAT, credit note no 770
29 Aug	Transfer of debit balance of £754.26 in the subsidiary (sales) ledger to Edge and Company's account in the subsidiary (purchases) ledger

You are to:

(a) prepare the accounts in the main ledger – including a purchases ledger control account – and subsidiary (purchases) ledger of Pembridge and Company and record the balances at 1 August 2004

(b) enter the above transactions in Pembridge's purchases day book and purchases returns day book for August 2004

(c) from the books of prime entry, record the accounting entries – including the set-off – in the main ledger and subsidiary (purchases) ledger, balancing all accounts at the month-end (31 August 2004)

(d) reconcile the control account balance with the subsidiary accounts at 1 August and 31 August 2004

13 MAKING PAYMENTS

13.1 You work as an assistant in the accounts department of A & S Systems Limited, computer consultants. Your job is to pay purchase invoices. Your file contains 12 invoices which have all been approved for payment.

The company writes out cheques in settlement of suppliers' invoices every week. It is company policy to pay strictly according to the terms of the invoice and to take advantage of settlement discounts whenever possible. Today is 27 March 2004.

You have been on holiday for a fortnight and someone else has done your job for the last two weeks. Your line manager suggests you check carefully to make sure your file is brought up to date and all outstanding invoices are settled, as he suspects some may have been overlooked.

You are to select the invoices due for payment and calculate the amount due on those invoices, taking into account any cash discount. A summary of the invoices is shown below.

invoice date	*supplier*	*terms*	*net*	*VAT*	*invoice total*
			£	£	£
11.02.04	James Smith Ltd	30 days	456.89	79.95	536.84
13.02.04	R Singh	30 days*	1,200.00	204.75	1,404.75
24.02.04	John Hopkins	30 days	230.75	40.38	271.13
24.02.04	Mereford Supplies	60 days	235.00	41.12	276.12
02.03.04	E Ragle Ltd	30 days	345.89	60.53	406.42
23.03.04	Meteor Ltd	30 days*	2,400.00	409.50	2,809.50
16.02.04	Helen Jarvis	30 days	109.00	19.07	128.07
17.02.04	Martley Electronics	60 days	245.00	42.87	287.87
24.03.04	Jones & Co	30 days*	950.00	162.09	1,112.09
20.02.04	J Marvell	30 days	80.95	14.16	95.11
19.02.04	K Nott	60 days	457.50	80.06	537.56
20.03.04	V Williams	30 days	1,250.00	218.75	1,468.75

* These invoices are marked '2.5% settlement discount for payment within 7 days'.

13.2 Complete the cheques shown on this and the next page in settlement of the invoices you have decided to pay. The date today is 27 March 2004. You will not sign the cheques; this will be done by two authorised signatories.

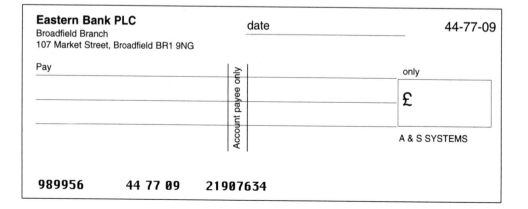

Eastern Bank PLC
Broadfield Branch
107 Market Street, Broadfield BR1 9NG

date 44-77-09

Pay

Account payee only

only

£

A & S SYSTEMS

989954 44 77 09 21907634

Eastern Bank PLC
Broadfield Branch
107 Market Street, Broadfield BR1 9NG

date 44-77-09

Pay

Account payee only

only

£

A & S SYSTEMS

989955 44 77 09 21907634

Eastern Bank PLC
Broadfield Branch
107 Market Street, Broadfield BR1 9NG

date 44-77-09

Pay

Account payee only

only

£

A & S SYSTEMS

989956 44 77 09 21907634

Eastern Bank PLC date 44-77-09
Broadfield Branch
107 Market Street, Broadfield BR1 9NG

Pay | Account payee only | only
£
A & S SYSTEMS

989957 44 77 09 21907634

Eastern Bank PLC date 44-77-09
Broadfield Branch
107 Market Street, Broadfield BR1 9NG

Pay | Account payee only | only
£
A & S SYSTEMS

989958 44 77 09 21907634

Eastern Bank PLC date 44-77-09
Broadfield Branch
107 Market Street, Broadfield BR1 9NG

Pay | Account payee only | only
£
A & S SYSTEMS

989959 44 77 09 21907634

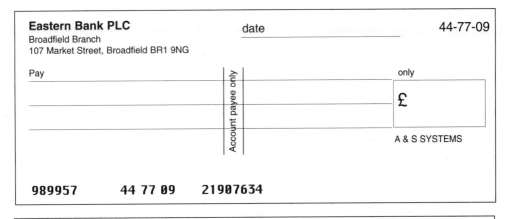

13.3 On 27 March 2004 your supervisor also asks you to arrange three payments: two wage cheques to new employees not yet on the computer payroll and a subscription to a professional organisation. You are to arrange these payments on the documents shown on the next page (you do not need to write out any cheques, or to sign the standing order). The details are as follows:

(a) Wages of £89.00 to R Power at Western Bank, Broadfield, Code 33 76 54, account number 71976234.

(b) Wages of £155.00 to R Patel at Central Bank, Broadfield, Code 88 76 51, account number 04892192.

(c) Monthly subscription of £15.00 (starting 1 April 2004, until further notice) to Association of Software Designers at Eastern Bank, Mereford, 44 77 06, account number 21903461, reference 121092.

Date		
Credit		
£50 notes		
£20 notes		
£10 notes		
£5 notes		
£2/£1		
50p		
20p		
10p,5p		
Bronze		
Total Cash		
Cheques etc		
£		

Date

Cashier's stamp and initials

Number of cheques

bank giro credit

Western Bank plc
Broadfield

Credit: R Power

Code: 33-76-54 Account: 71976234

Paid in by ____________

Do not write below this line

£50 notes		
£20 notes		
£10 notes		
£5 notes		
£2/£1		
50p		
20p		
10p,5p		
Bronze		
Total Cash		
Cheques etc		
£		

Date		
Credit		
£50 notes		
£20 notes		
£10 notes		
£5 notes		
£2/£1		
50p		
20p		
10p,5p		
Bronze		
Total Cash		
Cheques etc		
£		

Date

Cashier's stamp and initials

Number of cheques

bank giro credit

Central Bank PLC
Spring Gardens, Broadfield

Credit: R Patel

Code: 88-76-51 Account: 04892192

Paid in by ____________

Do not write below this line

£50 notes		
£20 notes		
£10 notes		
£5 notes		
£2/£1		
50p		
20p		
10p,5p		
Bronze		
Total Cash		
Cheques etc		
£		

STANDING ORDER MANDATE

To ____________ Bank

Address ____________

PLEASE PAY TO

Bank ____________ Branch ____________ Sort code [ ]

Beneficiary ____________ Account number [ ]

The sum of £ [ ] Amount in words ____________

Date of first payment ____________ Frequency of payment ____________

Until ____________ Reference ____________

Account to be debited [ ] Account number [ ]

SIGNATURE(S) ....

.... date..............................

14 PAYROLL PAYMENTS

14.1 Horne Electronics Limited employs twenty staff on its weekly payroll. They work a basic 35 hour week and are paid time-and-a-half for overtime. The basic pay rates are as follows:

Line manager: £7.50 per hour

Production staff: Grade 1 £6.00 per hour; Grade 2 £5.00 per hour

Clerical staff: Grade 1 £6.00 per hour; Grade 2 £5.50 per hour

During the course of one week the weekly paid staff work the following hours:

SUPERVISORS		***PRODUCTION STAFF***		***CLERICAL STAFF***	
J Plant	37 hours	***Grade 1***		***Grade 1***	
R Nott	36 hours	R Singh	35 hours	S Rozier	35 hours
		L Watt	38 hours	H James	36 hours
		J Weston	37 hours	R Pratt	38 hours
		Grade 2		***Grade 2***	
		L Curzon	35 hours	N Tamplin	40 hours
		N Serpel	36 hours	P Sargeant	36 hours
		E Smithson	39 hours	T Rotter	35 hours
		T Rothstein	36 hours	L Purcell	36 hours
		R Peggio	37 hours	R Patel	35 hours
		K West	41 hours	N Moore	37 hours

You are to calculate the gross pay of each weekly paid employee. Use the form on the next page.

employee	basic hours	basic pay £	overtime hours	overtime pay £	total gross pay £
Supervisors					
J Plant					
R Nott					
Production staff					
R Singh					
L Watt					
J Weston					
L Curzon					
N Serpel					
E Smithson					
T Rothstein					
R Peggio					
K West					
Clerical staff					
S Rozier					
H James					
R Pratt					
N Tamplin					
P Sargeant					
T Rotter					
L Purcell					
R Patel					
N Moore					

14.2 Horne Electronics employs ten monthly paid staff who are at executive and managerial levels. They are on the following pay scale:

Scale	*Annual Salary (£)*	*Employees*
1	12,500	T Restdale, Y Crouch, H Perkins, J Hampson
2	15,000	K Pantone, R Pettit
3	17,500	S Matthews, R Forrester
4	20,000	J Wibley
5	25,000	K Horne

It is the first month of the tax year and salaried staff have been given a productivity bonus of 5% of their gross annual salary. They have also been given the overtime shown below.

You are to calculate for each salaried employee:

(a) the basic gross monthly salary of each of the ten salaried staff (round to the nearest penny)

(b) the seasonal bonus

(c) the total gross monthly pay

Use the form set out below.

employee	annual salary £	monthly pay £	overtime £	bonus £	total monthly pay £
T Restdale			45.00		
Y Crouch			65.50		
H Perkins			none		
J Hampson			28.50		
K Pantone			none		
R Pettit			15.50		
S Matthews			16.00		
R Forrester			none		
J Wibley			none		
K Horne			none		

14.3 You are asked to work out the net annual pay of some of the salaried employees of Horne Electronics in Activity 14.2. Note that these tax and NIC rates are notional only.

They all have a Personal Tax Allowance of £4500 a year.

Tax is payable at 10% on the first £500 of taxable pay and at 22% on the remainder.

They all pay National Insurance Contributions at a rate of 10% per annum on their gross pay apart from the first £350 a month which is free of deductions.

(a) You are to work out their annual net pay on the table set out below.

employee	annual gross pay £	annual taxable pay £	tax @10% £	tax @ 22% £	NIC £	annual net pay £
J Hampson	12,500					
K Pantone	15,000					
S Matthews	17,500					
J Wibley	20,000					
K Horne	25,000					

(b) You receive notice from the Inland Revenue that K Horne's tax code has been reduced to 400L, which means that his Personal Allowance is reduced to £4,000 a year. What is his annual net pay after this change?

employee	annual gross pay £	annual taxable pay £	tax @10% £	tax @ 22% £	NIC £	annual net pay £
K Horne	25,000					

14.4 Osborne Electronics has six staff on the weekly payroll, all of whom are paid in cash. You have just drawn up the Week 7 payroll analysis sheet, an extract from which is shown on the next page. You are to complete a cash analysis for the six employees. The highest value notes and coins should be used, but no more than two £50 notes should be included in any pay packet.

OSBORNE ELECTRONICS		payroll analysis sheet									tax week 7	
employee reference	employee name	Earnings				Deductions				Employer's National Insurance Contributions £	Employer's Pension Contributions £	Net Pay £
		Basic £	Overtime £	Bonus £	Total Gross Pay £	Income Tax £	National Insurance £	Pension Contributions £	Total Deductions £			
2345	W Rowberry	205.00	25.00	15.00	245.00	35.00	19.50	10.25	64.75	24.50	10.25	180.25
2346	M Richardson	205.00	10.00	15.00	230.00	32.50	18.00	10.25	60.75	23.05	10.25	169.25
2347	D Stanbury	205.00	35.00	15.00	255.00	37.00	20.50	-	57.50	25.50	-	197.50
2348	D Payne	205.00	25.00	15.00	245.00	35.00	19.50	-	54.50	24.50	-	190.50
2349	K Peters	205.00	10.00	15.00	230.00	32.50	18.00	-	50.50	23.05	-	179.50
2350	O Robinson	205.00	15.00	15.00	235.00	34.00	18.50	10.25	62.75	24.50	10.25	172.25
TOTALS		1230.00	120.00	90.00	1440.00	206.00	114.00	30.75	350.75	145.10	30.75	1089.25

cash analysis sheet

tax week..................

OSBORNE ELECTRONICS

name	£50	£20	£10	£5	£2	£1	50p	20p	10p	5p	2p	1p	total
NUMBER													
TOTAL (£.p)													

14.5 Osborne Electronics also has three staff on the weekly payroll who are paid by cheque. You are to make out cheques *ready for signing* for the following employees (use today's date):

F Musgrave	£256.75
H Broadhurst	£189.79
L Wright	£246.43

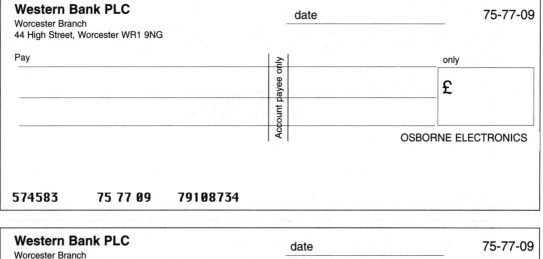

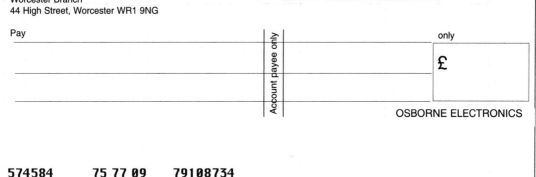

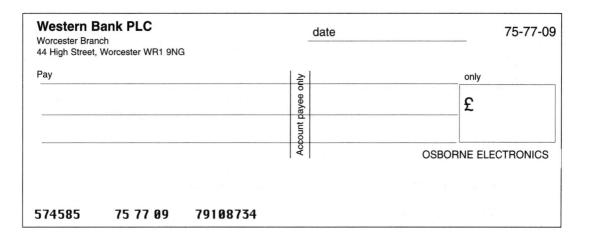

Western Bank PLC
Worcester Branch
44 High Street, Worcester WR1 9NG

date 75-77-09

Pay

Account payee only

only

£

OSBORNE ELECTRONICS

574583 75 77 09 79108734

Western Bank PLC
Worcester Branch
44 High Street, Worcester WR1 9NG

date 75-77-09

Pay

Account payee only

only

£

OSBORNE ELECTRONICS

574584 75 77 09 79108734

Western Bank PLC
Worcester Branch
44 High Street, Worcester WR1 9NG

date 75-77-09

Pay

Account payee only

only

£

OSBORNE ELECTRONICS

574585 75 77 09 79108734

14.6 Three new staff taken on by Osborne Electronics have been placed on a BACS 'auto credit' system. The details of the staff and the next month's pay are:

employee	*payee number*	*sort code*	*account no*	*amount (£)*
J Lloyd	456	40 40 40	12826251	786.00
H Thin	457	30 40 50	42447998	899.50
L Bright	458	20 87 65	80975132	885.75

Complete the schedule shown below, ready for signature. The payments should reach the bank accounts on the last working day of next month (based on today's date). The company reference is OE3452.

WESTERN BANK PLC
Auto Credit System

Bank branch..

Originator name...Reference................................

Date...............................

Branch	*Account no*	*Name*	*Payee no*	*Amount*
		PAYMENT TOTAL		

Please make the above payments to reach the payees on ....(date)

Please debit account no...............................with the sum of £...............................

Authorised signature...

14.7 You work in the Wages Office of Weatherbury Publications. It is 8 May 2004, just after the end of tax Month 1, and you have processed the payroll of the staff who are all on a monthly BACS wages payment scheme.

The wages have already been paid and the entries made in the ledger.

You have been allocated the task of making the monthly cheque payment to the Inland Revenue; the payment is due by 19 May.

The payroll summary shows the following figures:

employee	*gross pay* £	*National Insurance* £	*income tax* £
G Oak	1,070.00	192.16	154.84
B Everdene	1,708.23	319.36	301.58
D Venn	1,032.60	184.16	146.10
E Vye	1,433.50	264.16	238.33
S Smith	1,392.50	256.26	228.90
R Priddle	991.40	165.16	136.67
A Clare	1,459.60	269.76	244.31
T Durbeyfield	853.75	115.60	104.93
M South	1,067.00	191.36	154.15
F Day	656.78	76.16	59.62
J Fawley	932.88	164.16	123.10
S Bridehead	1,063.40	190.56	153.25
TOTALS (£)			

You are to

(a) Calculate the totals of the National Insurance and income tax columns on the summary form.

(b) Transfer these totals to the Inland Revenue P30B paying-in slip on the next page. The form should be completed ready for signature and paying in on 14 May.

(c) Complete the cheque on the next page. Make it payable to the Inland Revenue and ready for signature.

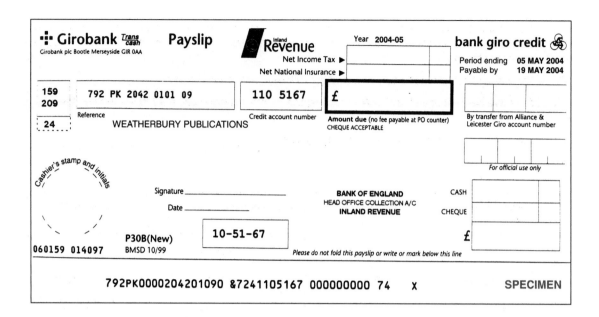

Girobank Transcash **Payslip**

Girobank plc Bootle Merseyside GIR 0AA

Inland Revenue

Year 2004-05

Net Income Tax ▶

Net National Insurance ▶

bank giro credit

Period ending **05 MAY 2004**

Payable by **19 MAY 2004**

159
209

792 PK 2042 0101 09

110 5167

£

24

Reference

WEATHERBURY PUBLICATIONS

Credit account number

Amount due (no fee payable at PO counter)
CHEQUE ACCEPTABLE

By transfer from Alliance & Leicester Giro account number

For official use only

Cashier's stamp and initials

Signature ______________________

Date ______________

BANK OF ENGLAND
HEAD OFFICE COLLECTION A/C
INLAND REVENUE

CASH

CHEQUE

£

P30B(New)
BMSD 10/99

10-51-67

060159 014097

Please do not fold this payslip or write or mark below this line

792PK0000204201090 &7241105167 000000000 74 X

SPECIMEN

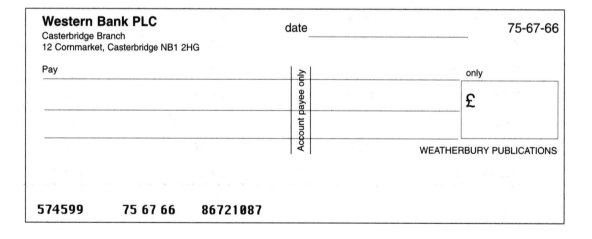

Western Bank PLC
Casterbridge Branch
12 Cornmarket, Casterbridge NB1 2HG

date ______________________

75-67-66

Pay ______________________ only

Account payee only

£

WEATHERBURY PUBLICATIONS

574599 75 67 66 86721087

15 CASH BOOK – RECORDING PAYMENTS

15.1 The discount received column of the cash book is totalled at regular intervals and transferred to:

(a) the debit side of discount received account

(b) the credit side of discount received account

(c) the credit side of general expenses account

(d) the debit side of general expenses account

Answer (a) or (b) or (c) or (d)

15.2 The VAT column on the payments side of the cash book is totalled at regular intervals and transferred to:

(a) the credit side of VAT account

(b) the credit side of sales account

(c) the debit side of VAT account

(d) the debit side of general expenses account

Answer (a) or (b) or (c) or (d)

15.3 You work as the cashier for Middleton Trading Company. A work experience student from the local college is with you today. You show the student the payments side of the cash book with last week's transactions as follows:

Credit			**Cash Book: Payments**			**CBP 36**
Date	Details	Folio	Discount received	VAT	Cash	Bank
2004			£	£	£	£
1 Oct	Balance b/d					1,588
1 Oct	Teme Traders	PL				585
2 Oct	Insurance	ML				250
2 Oct	Office stationery	ML		14	94	
3 Oct	Tyax Supplies	PL	10			190
4 Oct	Purchases	ML		21		141
5 Oct	Wages	ML			455	
			10	35	549	2,754

You are to explain to the student what each of the transactions represents and the other accounting entries involved in the transactions. Note that the company's book-keeping system includes a purchases ledger control account.

15.4 The following are the payments transactions of Marcle Enterprises for October 2004:

3 Oct	Cash purchases paid for by cheque, £440 + VAT
5 Oct	Paid Jarvis Supplies a cheque for £625 in full settlement of a debt of £645
8 Oct	Bought office equipment, paying by cheque £320 + VAT
12 Oct	Paid Hallam Limited £237 by cheque
16 Oct	Paid salaries by BACS, £2,247 (no VAT)
18 Oct	Paid telephone expenses by cheque, £329 (including VAT)
22 Oct	Paid T Woods a cheque for £439 in full settlement of a debt of £449
24 Oct	Cash purchases paid for by cheque, £400 + VAT
26 Oct	Paid wages in cash, £420 (no VAT)
29 Oct	The owner of the business withdraws £500 by cheque for own use
30 Oct	Cash purchases paid for in cash, £120 + VAT

The rate of Value Added Tax is 17.5%.

Account numbers are to be used – see below.

You are to:

- Enter the above payments on page 67 of the three column cash book of Marcle Enterprises.
- Sub-total the money columns at 31 October.
- Show the entries to be made in the following accounts:

subsidiary (purchases) ledger

Hallam Limited (account no 455)

Jarvis Supplies (account no 525)

T Woods (account no 760)

main ledger

purchases ledger control account (account no 6002)

discount received account (account no 6502)

drawings account (account no 7005)

office equipment account (account no 750)

purchases account (account no 5001)

telephone expenses account (account no 6212)

VAT account (account no 2200)

wages and salaries account (account no 7750)

15.5 The following are the payments transactions of Kendrick and Company for November 2004:

5 Nov	Cash purchases paid for by cheque, £235 (including VAT)
7 Nov	Bought office stationery £40 + VAT, paying in cash
9 Nov	Paid a cheque for £355 to Abel and Company, a creditor, in full settlement of an invoice for £370
12 Nov	Cash purchases for £141 (including VAT) paid in cash
13 Nov	Bought office equipment, paying by cheque, £360 + VAT
15 Nov	Paid an invoice for £250 from A Palmer, a creditor, by cheque for £235, £15 being received for prompt settlement
16 Nov	Loan repayment of £250 made to HSCB Bank by direct debit (no VAT)
19 Nov	The owners of the business withdraw £400 by cheque for own use
21 Nov	Cash purchases of £94 (including VAT) paid in cash
26 Nov	Paid a cheque for £325 to P Singh Limited, a creditor, in full settlement of an invoice for £335
27 Nov	Paid salaries by BACS, £1,552 (no VAT)
28 Nov	Cash purchases of £240 + VAT, paid by cheque
29 Nov	Paid wages in cash, £475 (no VAT)
29 Nov	Paid a cheque for £340 to Abel and Company, a creditor, in full settlement of an invoice for £350
30 Nov	Bought office stationery £120 + VAT, paying by cheque

The rate of Value Added Tax is 17.5%
Account numbers are to be used – see below.

You are to:

- Enter the above payments on page 24 of the cash book of Kendrick and Company, using columns for date, details, folio, discount received, VAT, cash and bank.
- Sub-total the money columns at 30 November.
- Show the entries to be made in the following accounts:

subsidiary (purchases) ledger

Abel and Company (account no 105)
A Palmer (account no 495)
P Singh Limited (account no 645)

main ledger

purchases ledger control account (account no 6002)
discount received account (account no 6502)
drawings account (account no 7005)
loan account: HSCB Bank (account no 2250)
office equipment account (account no 750)
office stationery account (account no 6384)
purchases account (account no 5001)
VAT account (account no 2200)
wages and salaries account (account no 7750)

15.6 Martin Peters runs a building supplies company. He buys in bulk from manufacturers and sells in smaller quantities to trade customers on credit and to the public on cash terms. His business is registered for VAT.

He uses a cash book which analyses payments between:

- discount received
- VAT
- cash purchases
- subsidiary (purchases) ledger
- wages and salaries
- sundry

The following transactions take place during the week commencing 19 November 2004:

19 Nov	Cash purchases of £150.00 (including VAT) paid by cheque
19 Nov	Paid an invoice for £292.65 from Broughton Brick Company (a creditor) by cheque for £286.40 and receiving £6.25 discount for prompt settlement
20 Nov	Bought stationery £45.50 (including VAT), paying in cash
21 Nov	Paid an invoice for £552.70 from Broad Timber Limited (a creditor) by cheque
21 Nov	Bought central heating oil £124.04 + VAT, paying by cheque
22 Nov	Paid wages £182.31 in cash (no VAT)
23 Nov	Cash purchases of £80.00 (including VAT) paid for in cash
23 Nov	Paid salaries by BACS, £1,357.00 (no VAT)
23 Nov	Paid an invoice for £468.25 from Wyvern Cement Company (a creditor) by cheque for £458.25 and receiving £10.00 discount for prompt settlement
23 Nov	Bought stationery £85.25 + VAT, paying by cheque
23 Nov	Cash purchases of £340.40 (including VAT) paid for in cash

The rate of Value Added Tax is 17.5%

Account numbers are to be used as follows:

Main ledger account codes (extract):	
1000	Cash book
2500	Purchases ledger control
3500	Discount received
4500	Purchases
6000	VAT
7000	Salaries and wages
7500	Sundry

Subsidiary (purchases) ledger account codes (extract):	
120	Broughton Brick Company
150	Broad Timber Limited
890	Wyvern Cement

Using the layouts on the next three pages, you are to:

- Enter the above payments on page 45 of the analysed cash book of Martin Peters (VAT amounts should be rounded down to the nearest penny).
- Total the money columns at 23 November.
- Show the entries to be made in the main ledger and the subsidiary (purchases) ledger.

ACCOUNT NO 1000 CASH BOOK (PAYMENTS)

CBP 45

Date	Details	Reference	Cash	Bank	Discount received	VAT	Cash purchases	Subsidiary (purchases) ledger	Salaries and wages	Sundry	Subsidiary (purchases) ledger code
2004			£	£	£	£	£	£	£	£	
	Main ledger codes	DR									
		CR									

MAIN LEDGER

2500 Purchases Ledger Control

Date	Details	Folio	Amount	Date	Details	Folio	Amount
2004			£	2004			£

3500 Discount Received

Date	Details	Folio	Amount	Date	Details	Folio	Amount
2004			£	2004			£

4500 Purchases

Date	Details	Folio	Amount	Date	Details	Folio	Amount
2004			£	2004			£

6000 VAT

Date	Details	Folio	Amount	Date	Details	Folio	Amount
2004			£	2004			£

7000 Salaries and Wages

Date	Details	Folio	Amount	Date	Details	Folio	Amount
2004			£	2004			£

MAIN LEDGER

7500 Sundry

Date	Details	Folio	Amount	Date	Details	Folio	Amount
2004			£	2004			£

SUBSIDIARY (PURCHASES) LEDGER

120 Broughton Brick Company

Date	Details	Folio	Amount	Date	Details	Folio	Amount
2004			£	2004			£

150 Broad Timber Limited

Date	Details	Folio	Amount	Date	Details	Folio	Amount
2004			£	2004			£

890 Wyvern Cement

Date	Details	Folio	Amount	Date	Details	Folio	Amount
2004			£	2004			£

16 PETTY CASH BOOK

16.1 A company operates its petty cash book using the imprest system. The imprest amount is £250.00. At the end of a particular period the analysis columns are totalled to give the following amounts:

VAT £13.42; postages £29.18; travel £45.47; stationery £33.29; sundry £18.54

How much cash will be required to restore the imprest amount for the next period?

16.2 You work as an accounts assistant in the offices of Hi-Tech Trading Company, a VAT-registered business. One of your responsibilities is to maintain the petty cash records and you are authorised to approve petty cash vouchers up to a value of £20 each. How will you deal with the following discrepancies and queries?

- A petty cash voucher for stationery is submitted to you for £12.50; the till receipt from the stationery shop shows a total of £10.00.
- A petty cash voucher for travelling expenses is submitted to you for £25.50; a rail ticket for this value is attached.
- The total of the analysis columns of the petty cash book differs from the total payments column.
- A colleague asks about the imprest amount and where you keep the keys to the petty cash box.

16.3 The cashier where you work as an accounts assistant has asked you to balance the petty cash book for the week ending 16 May 2004. The petty cash book is kept on the imprest system and, at the end of each week, cash is withdrawn from the main cash book to restore the imprest amount to £100.00.

The petty cash book is as follows:

Receipts	Date	Details	Voucher	Total	Analysis columns				
			No	Payment	VAT	Postages	Travel	Meals	Stationery
£	2004			£	£	£	£	£	£
100.00	12 May	Balance b/d							
	12 May	Travel	461	6.50			6.50		
	13 May	Meal allowance	462	6.11				6.11	
	13 May	Stationery	463	8.46	1.26				7.20
	13 May	Taxi	464	5.17	0.77		4.40		
	14 May	Stationery	465	4.70	0.70				4.00
	14 May	Travel	466	3.50			3.50		
	14 May	Postages	467	4.50		4.50			
	15 May	Bus fares	468	3.80			3.80		
	15 May	Catering	469	10.81	1.61			9.20	
	16 May	Postages	470	3.50		3.50			
	16 May	Stationery	471	7.52	1.12				6.40
	16 May	Travel	472	6.45			6.45		

You are to:

- restore the imprest amount of petty cash to £100.00, making the appropriate entry (note: the main cash book entry for this transaction need not be shown)
- balance the petty cash book at 16 May 2004, bringing down the balance on 17 May

16.4 You work as an accounts assistant in the offices of Wyvern Printers plc, a company which specialises in printing colour supplements for newspapers. Your supervisor is the main cashier. One of your tasks includes responsibility for all aspects of petty cash.

The accounting procedures manual of Wyvern Printers includes the following references to petty cash:

- A petty cash book is to be maintained using the imprest system.
- The imprest amount at the beginning of each week is to be £250.
- The maximum amount which can be drawn from petty cash is £50 in any one transaction.
- The petty cashier can authorise petty cash vouchers up to £25 for any one transaction; amounts above £25 and up to £50 can be authorised by the main cashier.
- All petty cash transactions must be recorded on petty cash vouchers which are to be
  - numbered in sequence
  - accompanied by relevant supporting documentation
- Authorised petty cash vouchers are to be recorded in a petty cash book with analysis columns for Value Added Tax, Postages, Travel, Stationery, Sundries.
- At the end of each week
  - cash is to be drawn from the main cashier to restore the imprest amount
  - the petty cash book is to be balanced ready for the following week
  - a posting sheet is to be prepared and passed to the main cashier

In addition you know that petty cash claims include VAT at the current rate of 17.5%, except for postages, rail and bus travel, newspapers and magazines which are either zero-rated or exempt from VAT.

During the week commencing 15 January 2004 several petty cash vouchers, together with supporting documentation, are passed to you by members of staff. The petty cash vouchers are shown on the next two pages, and the supporting documentation on the two pages following (pages 87 and 88).

You are to:

- Refer to the petty cash vouchers and supporting documentation – on the next four pages – and, for each claim you are satisfied with, you are to sign in the 'authorised' section; the authorised vouchers are to be numbered in sequence beginning with the number 352.
- For any petty cash claims you are unable to process, you are to write a memorandum to the main cashier explaining the reasons.
- Write up the petty cash book for the week commencing 15 January 2004 starting with an imprest balance of £250, and recording the petty cash vouchers that you have authorised.

- Total the analysis columns and prepare a posting sheet which shows the entries to be recorded in the main ledger at the end of the week, on 19 January. Account numbers need not be shown.
- Restore the imprest amount of petty cash to £250.00 by transfer from the cash book.
- Balance the petty cash book at 19 January 2004 and bring down the balance on 22 January.

Vouchers for the week beginning 15 January 2004 (continued on the next page)

petty cash voucher number _ _
date *18 Jan 2004*

description	amount £	p
Postages	*25*	*25*
	25	*25*

signature *M. Gono*
authorised

petty cash voucher number _ _
date *18 Jan 2004*

description	amount £	p
Stationery	*14*	*10*
	14	*10*

signature *J. Jones*
authorised

petty cash voucher number _ _
date *18 Jan 2004*

description	amount £	p
Taxi fare	*4*	*70*
	4	*70*

signature *J. Jones*
authorised

petty cash voucher number _ _
date *18 Jan 2004*

description	amount £	p
Meal allowance	*6*	*11*
	6	*11*

signature *R. Singh*
authorised

petty cash voucher number _ _
date *17 Jan 2004*

description	amount £	p
Travel	*22*	*85*
	22	*85*

signature *J. Jones*
authorised

petty cash voucher number _ _
date *17 Jan 2004*

description	amount £	p
Postages	*17*	*00*
	17	*00*

signature *J. Jones*
authorised

petty cash voucher number _ _

date *16 Jan 2004*

description	amount £	amount p
Travel	*13*	*50*
	13	*50*

signature *M. Gono*

authorised

petty cash voucher number _ _

date *16 Jan 2004*

description	amount £	amount p
Taxi	*5*	*17*
	5	*17*

signature *J. Jones*

authorised

petty cash voucher number _ _

date *16 Jan 2004*

description	amount £	amount p
Stationery	*4*	*70*
	4	*70*

signature *J. Jones*

authorised

petty cash voucher number _ _

date *15 Jan 2004*

description	amount £	amount p
Stationery	*8*	*46*
	8	*46*

signature *R. Singh*

authorised

petty cash voucher number _ _

date *15 Jan 2004*

description	amount £	amount p
Meal allowance	*6*	*11*
	6	*11*

signature *J. Jones*

authorised

petty cash voucher number _ _

date *15 Jan 2004*

description	amount £	amount p
Travel	*16*	*50*
	16	*50*

signature *J. Jones*

authorised

Western Trains plc
PO Box 731, Weston WS1 1QQ
RECEIPT FOR RAIL TICKETS

Amount £ 16.50
Date 15 Jan 2004
Issued by H Vaz

Western Trains – working towards excellence

Wyvern Printers plc
MEAL ALLOWANCE

Date 15/1/04
Name J. JONES
Amount £ 6.11
Authorised by L. Luz, Manager
Department code 08

Stationery Suppliers Limited
8 High Street, Wyvern WV1 2AP
VAT registration: 491 7681 20

15 01 2004

Goods	7.20
VAT	1.26
Total	8.46
Tendered	10.00
Change	1.54

Please call again!

Crown Taxis
20 Lime Street, Wyvern WV3 1DS
Telephone: 01901 436941

Date 16/1/04
Received with thanks £ 5.17

VAT registration: 495 7681 21

Stationery Suppliers Limited
8 High Street, Wyvern WV1 2AP
VAT registration: 491 7681 20

16 01 2004

Goods	4.00
VAT	0.70
Total	4.70
Tendered	10.00
Change	5.30

Please call again!

Western Trains plc
PO Box 731, Weston WS1 1QQ
RECEIPT FOR RAIL TICKETS

Amount £ 13.50
Date 17/01/04
Issued by J. Clark

Western Trains – working towards excellence

POST OFFICE COUNTERS LTD
WYVERN HIGH STREET POSTSHOP
VAT REG 647240004 BRANCH NO 0096

15/01/2004	1027
Parcel post	
Total to pay	17.00
Cash tendered	20.00
Change	3.00

DON'T FORGET VALENTINE'S DAY!
14th FEBRUARY

Western Trains plc
PO Box 731, Weston WS1 1QQ
RECEIPT FOR RAIL TICKETS

Amount	£ *22.85*
Date	*17 Jan 2004*
Issued by	*H Vaz*

Western Trains – working towards excellence

Wyvern Printers plc
MEAL ALLOWANCE

Date	*18 Jan 2004*
Name	*R. SINGH*
Amount	£ *6.11*
Authorised by	*A. Eden, Manager*
Department code	*12*

Crown Taxis
20 Lime Street, Wyvern WV3 1DS
Telephone: 01901 436941

Date	*18 Jan 2004*
Received with thanks	£ *4.70*

VAT registration: 495 7681 21

Stationery Suppliers Limited
8 High Street, Wyvern WV1 2AP
VAT registration: 491 7681 20

18 01 2004

Goods	12.00
VAT	2.10
Total	14.10
Tendered	20.00
Change	6.90

Please call again!

POST OFFICE COUNTERS LTD
WYVERN HIGH STREET POSTSHOP
VAT REG 647240004 BRANCH NO 0096

18/01/2004	1536
Stamps	
Total to pay	25.25
Cash tendered	30.00
Change	4.75

DON'T FORGET VALENTINE'S DAY!
14th FEBRUARY

17 FURTHER ASPECTS OF DOUBLE-ENTRY ACCOUNTS

17.1 Tom Griffiths set up in business on 1 March 2004 and registered for Value Added Tax. During the first month he has kept a cash book but, unfortunately, has made some errors:

Debit		**Cash Book: Receipts**			**CBR**
Date	Details	Folio	Discount allowed	Cash	Bank
2004			£	£	£
4 Mar	Office equipment*				1,175
12 Mar	Drawings			125	

Credit		**Cash Book: Payments**			**CBP**
Date	Details	Folio	Discount received	Cash	Bank
2004			£	£	£
3 Mar	Capital				6,500
5 Mar	Bank loan				2,500
7 Mar	Wages				250
10 Mar	Commission received*			141	
12 Mar	Rent paid				200
17 Mar	Van*				7.050

The items with asterisks (*) include Value Added Tax

Tom Griffiths has not got around to the other double-entry accounts.

You are to rewrite the cash book of Tom Griffiths, putting right his errors, and to draw up the other accounts, making the appropriate entries.

Notes:

- Use the current rate of Value Added Tax (17.5 % at the time of writing)
- Account numbers need not be used
- Separate books of prime entry need not be shown

17.2 Enter the following transactions into the double-entry book-keeping accounts of Caroline Yates, who is registered for Value Added Tax. Include a cash book receipts and a cash book payments, both with columns for cash and bank.

2004	
3 Nov	Started in business with capital of £75,000 in the bank
4 Nov	Bought a photocopier for £2,400 + VAT, paying by cheque
7 Nov	Received a bank loan of £70,000
10 Nov	Bought office premises £130,000, paying by cheque
12 Nov	Paid rates of £3,000, by cheque
14 Nov	Bought office fittings £1,520 + VAT, paying by cheque
17 Nov	Received commission of £400 + VAT, in cash
18 Nov	Drawings in cash £125
20 Nov	Paid wages £250, by cheque
25 Nov	Returned some of the office fittings (unsuitable) and received a refund cheque for £200 + VAT
28 Nov	Received commission £200 + VAT, by cheque

Notes:

- Use the current rate of Value Added Tax (17.5% at the time of writing)
- Account numbers need not be used
- Separate books of prime entry need not be shown

17.3 A friend of yours, Natasha Williams, runs a catering business which supplies food and drink to companies for special events. You keep the 'books' of the business which is registered for VAT.

Natasha tells you about a customer, Mereford Marketing, for whom she provided tea and coffee for their stand at the 'Two Counties Spring Show'. Despite sending monthly statements of account and 'chaser' letters she has still not been paid, and has recently heard that they have gone out of business. It is now 18 December 2004 and Natasha doesn't think she will be able to collect the amount due and asks you to write off the account as a bad debt.

You look up the account in the subsidiary (sales) ledger:

Dr		**Mereford Marketing**			Cr
2004		£	2004		£
25 Apr	Sales	141			

Natasha reminds you that, as VAT was charged on the original invoice, VAT can be reclaimed when writing off that debt.

You are to show:

- the journal entry made on 18 December 2004
- the transactions on Mereford Marketing's account in the subsidiary (sales) ledger
- bad debts written off account in the main ledger
- VAT account in the main ledger
- sales ledger control account in the main ledger

Note: account numbers need not be used

17.4 You are an accounts assistant at Osborne Electronics. A work experience student from the local college is with you today. The owner of the business authorises you to show the student the following non-routine transactions which are going through the accounts today, 16 November 2004:

- office equipment has been bought for £1,200 + VAT and paid for by cheque
- the owner of the business has paid in additional capital, £2,500 by cheque (no VAT)
- the account of a debtor, Tintern Travel, with a balance of £188 is to be written off as a bad debt (VAT-relief is available)
- a loan of £1,000 (no VAT) has been received from David Nazir by cheque

You are to:

(a) Explain to the student what each transaction represents and the double-entry book-keeping involved.

(b) Prepare a posting sheet for the transactions (account numbers need not be used).

17.5 Classify the following costs as either *capital expenditure* or *revenue expenditure.*

		capital expenditure	revenue expenditure
(a)	building an extension to the factory		
(b)	repairs to the existing factory		
(c)	fuel for vehicles		
(d)	purchase cost of vehicles		
(e)	delivery cost of vehicles		
(f)	cost of own materials used to repair the office		
(g)	wages of own employees asked to carry out repairs to the office		
(h)	office salaries		

19 BALANCING THE CASH BOOK AND BANK RECONCILIATION

19.1 A firm's bank statement shows an overdraft of £600. Unpresented cheques total £250; outstanding lodgements total £1,000. What is the balance shown by the firm's cash book?

(a) £150

(b) £650

(c) £250 overdraft

(d) £150 overdraft

Answer (a) or (b) or (c) or (d)

19.2 Upon receipt of a bank statement, which one of the following must be written into the firm's cash book?

(a) cheque debited in error by the bank

(b) unpresented cheques

(c) BACS receipts

(d) outstanding lodgements

Answer (a) or (b) or (c) or (d)

19.3 Heath Traders Limited requires the bank statement and cash book balances (bank columns) to be reconciled. You are given the following information as at 30 June 2004:

- the bank columns of the cash book show an overdraft of £1,250 at the bank
- cheques for £140, £110 and £60 have been sent out in payment to various suppliers but have not yet been paid into the bank by those suppliers; they are recorded in the cash book
- a direct debit payment of £40 has been recorded by the bank, but has not yet been entered in the cash book
- a cheque for £600 has been recorded as a receipt in the cash book, and paid into the bank; it has not yet been credited by the bank
- bank charges amounting to £25 appear on the bank statement, but have not yet been entered in the cash book
- a BACS receipt from a customer for £250 appears on the bank statement, but has not yet been entered in the cash book
- the bank statement shows a closing bank overdraft of £1,355

You are to:

(a) write the cash book up-to-date at 30 June 2004

(b) prepare a bank reconciliation statement at 30 June 2004 which agrees the bank statement balance with the cash book balance

19.4 The bank columns of David Smith's cash book for March 2004 are as follows:

2004	*Receipts*	£	2004	*Payments*		£
1 Mar	Balance b/d	755.50	4 Mar	Curtis Ltd	001531	200.00
8 Mar	Johnson Limited	530.90	12 Mar	T Daniels	001532	327.40
29 Mar	Reid & Co	386.45	15 Mar	Smith & Co	001533	289.60
			16 Mar	Arnold & Sons	001534	327.20
			22 Mar	P Singh	001535	154.30

He received his bank statement which showed the following transactions for March 2004:

BANK STATEMENT				
Date	Details	Payments	Receipts	Balance
2004		£	£	£
1 Mar	Balance brought forward			855.50 CR
5 Mar	Cheque no 001530	100.00		755.50 CR
8 Mar	Cheque no 001531	200.00		555.50 CR
8 Mar	Credit		530.90	1,086.40 CR
15 Mar	BACS receipt: A J Trading		396.20	1,482.60 CR
22 Mar	Cheque no 001532	327.40		1,155.20 CR
24 Mar	Direct debit: Arley Finance	184.65		970.55 CR
25 Mar	Cheque no 001533	289.60		680.95 CR

You are to:

(a) write the cash book up-to-date at 31 March 2004, and show the balance carried down

(b) prepare a bank reconciliation statement at 31 March 2004 which agrees the bank statement balance with the cash book balance

19.5 You are the trainee cashier at Durning Traders Limited, working under the supervision of the office manager. The bank columns of the company's cash book for the week commencing 7 June 2004 are as follows:

2004	*Receipts*	£	2004	*Payments*		£
7 Jun	Balance b/d	986.40	7 Jun	Mega Books Ltd	654321	406.29
7 Jun	Wyvern Council	428.15	7 Jun	Cash	654322	250.00
10 Jun	Abacus & Co	752.00	8 Jun	Western Telecom	654323	186.45
10 Jun	ITI Plc	552.16	10 Jun	Wages	654324	522.15
			11 Jun	College Supplies Ltd	654325	342.87

The bank statement was received which showed the following transactions for the week:

BANK STATEMENT				
Date	Details	Payments	Receipts	Balance
2004		£	£	£
7 Jun	Balance brought forward			1,186.40 CR
7 Jun	Cheque no 654320	200.00		986.40 CR
7 Jun	Credit		428.15	1,414.55 CR
7 Jun	Cheque no 654322	250.00		1,164.55 CR
10 Jun	DD: Westmid Finance Co	107.25		1,057.30 CR
10 Jun	Cheque no 654324	522.15		535.15 CR
10 Jun	Credit		752.00	1,287.15 CR
10 Jun	BACS: Johnson Plc		398.52	1,685.67 CR
11 Jun	Cheque no 654321	406.29		1,279.38 CR
11 Jun	Cheque no 888901	50.00		1,229.38 CR
11 Jun	Bank charges	17.50		1,211.88 CR
SO Standing Order **DD** Direct Debit **BACS** Automated Transfer				

You are to:

(a) write the cash book up-to-date for the week commencing 7 June 2004, and show the balance carried down

(b) prepare a bank reconciliation statement at 11 June 2004 which agrees the bank statement balance with the cash book balance

(c) write a memorandum to the office manager regarding any matter that you think should be queried with the bank (use the blank memorandum printed on page 95)

MEMORANDUM

To

From

Date

19.6 You work as an accounts assistant in the office of Speciality Paints Limited, a company which buys special types of paints and other finishes from the manufacturers and sells them in your area to local businesses. This week the cashier, who is responsible for keeping the company's cash book is away on holiday. You have been asked to carry out her work for the week commencing 8 September 2004.

At the start of the week the cash book has a balance at bank of £802.50, and cash in hand of £120.68. The following are the transactions to be entered in the cash book for the week:

Cheques received from debtors

8 Sep	£389.51 from Wyvern County Council, in full settlement of an invoice for £398.01
10 Sep	£451.20 from J Jones & Company
12 Sep	£458.25 from Building Supplies Limited, in full settlement of an invoice for £468.25

Note: all cheques received are banked on the day of receipt.

Cheques drawn

8 Sep	Cheque no 123451 for £263.49, payee ITI Paint Division Limited, a creditor, in full settlement of an invoice for £269.24
9 Sep	Cheque no 123452 for £100.00, payee Wyvern Charities
9 Sep	Cheque no 123453 for £169.75, payee United Telecom plc
10 Sep	Cheque no 123454 for £394.20, payee Wages
11 Sep	Cheque no 123455 for £160.38, payee Paint Manufacturing plc, in full settlement of an invoice for £163.88

Cash received from debtors

9 Sep	£27.50 from T Lewis
12 Sep	£22.91 from H Simms, in full settlement of an invoice for £23.41

Cash paid

11 Sep	£88.50 for casual labour

At the end of the week, the bank statement, shown on the next page, is received.

You are to:

- enter the transactions for the week in the three-column (with columns for discount, cash, bank) cash book of Speciality Paints Limited
- check the bank statement and write the cash book (bank columns) up-to-date with any items appearing on the bank statement that need to be recorded in the cash book
- balance the cash book at 12 September 2004, and show the discount accounts as they will appear in the firm's main ledger
- prepare a bank reconciliation statement which agrees the bank statement balance with the cash book balance
- write a memorandum to the office manager regarding any matter that you consider should be queried with the bank (use the blank memorandum printed on page 98)

National Bank PLC

Branch Mereford

Account Speciality Paints Ltd

Account number 12345678 **Statement number** 45 **Date** 12 Sep 2004

Date	Details	Payments	Receipts	Balance
2004		£	£	£
8 Sep	Balance brought forward			802.50 Cr
8 Sep	Credit		389.51	1,192.01 Cr
9 Sep	Cheque 123452	100.00		1,092.01 Cr
9 Sep	DD Wyvern Hire Purchase	85.50		1,006.51 Cr
10 Sep	Cheque 123454	394.20		612.31 Cr
10 Sep	Credit		451.20	1,063.51 Cr
10 Sep	BACS Johnson & Co		125.50	1,189.01 Cr
11 Sep	Cheque 123451	263.49		925.52 Cr
11 Sep	Cheque 874111	25.00		900.52 Cr
12 Sep	Bank charges	12.50		888.02 Cr

SO Standing Order **DD** Direct Debit **BACS** Automated Transfer

MEMORANDUM

To

From

Date

20 USING THE JOURNAL AND RECONCILING CONTROL ACCOUNTS

20.1 Which one of the following transactions will be recorded in the journal?

(a) credit purchase of goods

(b) credit purchase of a fixed asset

(c) goods returned by a debtor

(d) cash sale of goods

Answer (a) or (b) or (c) or (d)

20.2 Which one of the following transactions will not be recorded in the journal?

(a) opening entries of a new business

(b) goods taken by the owner for her own use

(c) petty cash payment for office window cleaning

(d) writing off a bad debt

Answer (a) or (b) or (c) or (d)

20.3 Mohammed Pazir started in business on 1 February 2004 with the following assets and liabilities:

	£
Vehicle	6,500
Fixtures and fittings	2,800
Stock	4,100
Cash	150
Loan from uncle	5,000

You are to prepare Mohammed's opening journal entry showing clearly his capital at 1 February 2004.

20.4 Your friend, Sam Huntley, has recently set up in business selling electrical fittings and parts to both trade customers and members of the public. Her business is not yet registered for VAT.

You are helping Sam with the book-keeping. She has given you the list of business transactions shown on page 101 and asks for your help in identifying for each transaction:

- the book of prime entry
- the account to be debited
- the account to be credited

Her book-keeping system comprises a main ledger, with a subsidiary (sales) ledger and a subsidiary (purchases) ledger.

You are to complete the table on the next page with the information that Sam requires.

20.5 You work as an accounts assistant for James & Sons Limited. The company buys office furniture and stationery in bulk from the manufacturers and then sells smaller quantities on credit to local businesses.

Today the accounts supervisor has asked you to reconcile the sales ledger control account with the total of the subsidiary (sales) ledger. The information which follows is available to you.

Summary of transactions with credit customers in July 2004:

	£
Balance of debtors at 1 July 2004	64,626
Credit sales	72,310
Money received from credit customers	80,055
Discount allowed	90
Sales returns from credit customers	1,462
Bad debt written off	125

The following balances were shown in the subsidiary (sales) ledger at 31 July 2004:

	£	
A-Z Supplies Limited	8,394	debit
Doyle & Company	10,635	debit
Edgington and Sons	6,125	debit
Kernow Model Company	3,276	debit
Mereford Garden Centre	9,112	debit
Pembridge plc	13,236	debit
Wyvern Traders	4,516	debit

You are to:

(a) Prepare a sales ledger control account for July 2004 from the details above. The account is to be balanced at 31 July 2004 to show the balance carried down to next month.

(b) Reconcile the sales ledger control account with the total of the subsidiary ledger in the following format:

	£
Sales ledger control account balance as at 31 July 2004	
Total of subsidiary (sales) ledger accounts as at 31 July 2004	
Difference	

(c) If there is a difference calculated in (b) above, what do you think might have caused it?

20.4 See Activity on page 99

Business transaction	Book of prime entry	Account to be debited	Account to be credited
(a) sold goods on credit to Aztec Electrics			
(b) goods purchased on credit from United Supplies plc			
(c) Aztec Electrics returns faulty goods – a credit note is issued			
(d) bought office equipment on credit from Beacon Office Limited			
(e) sold goods for cash			
(f) Sam withdraws cash from the bank as drawings			
(g) wrote off an account in the subsidiary (sales) ledger as a bad debt			
(h) paid a creditor by cheque			

20.6 You work as an accounts assistant for Beacon Surf Limited. The company runs a large surf supplies shop overlooking a popular beach in Cornwall.

Today the accounts supervisor has asked you to reconcile the purchases ledger control account with the total of the subsidiary (purchases) ledger. The information which follows is available to you.

Summary of transactions with credit suppliers in May 2004:

	£
Balance of creditors at 1 May 2004	42,106
Goods purchased on credit	31,473
Paid creditors	25,236
Discount received	220
Goods returned to suppliers	2,048

The following balances were shown in the subsidiary (purchases) ledger at 31 May 2004:

	£	
Boards 'R Us	12,056	credit
Durning & Company	110	debit
Fistral Surf	4,872	credit
New Wave Limited	8,169	credit
Performance Clothing Limited	15,238	credit
Surf Supplies Limited	3,294	credit
Zelah Traders	2,996	credit

You are to:

(a) Prepare a purchases ledger control account for May 2004 from the details above. The account is to be balanced at 31 May 2004 to show the balance carried down to next month.

(b) Reconcile the purchases ledger control account with the total of the subsidiary ledger in the following format:

	£
Purchases ledger control account balance as at 31 May 2004	
Total of subsidiary (purchases) ledger accounts as at 31 May 2004	
Difference	

(c) If there is a difference calculated in (b) above, what do you think might have caused it?

20.7 Bissoe Limited keeps a petty cash control account in the main ledger and the petty cash book is the subsidiary account. Petty cash book is kept on the imprest method, and the imprest amount is £200.

The following petty cash transactions took place in June 2004:

1 Jun	Balance of petty cash book brought down, £200
30 Jun	Total of payments made from petty cash during the month, £111
30 Jun	Imprest amount restored by transfer from the bank

You are to:

(a) Enter the transactions for June 2004 into the firm's petty cash control account, showing clearly the balance carried down.

(b) State *one* other check you would carry out to ensure that the petty cash book is correct.

20.8 Nazir Limited rents out part of its property to five tenants. In the main ledger it has a rent receivable control account; the subsidiary (non-trade debtors) ledger contains accounts in the name of each of its tenants.

The following is a summary of rent receivable activities during the month of June 2004:

	£	
Balance of non-trade debtors at 1 June	550	debit
Rent receivable for the month	3,450	
Money received from tenants	3,600	
Journal debit to correct an error	100	

The following closing balances were in the subsidiary (non-trade debtors) ledger on 30 June 2004:

	£	
Aztec Traders	150	debit
Baig Associates	50	debit
Martinez and Company	225	debit
Perran Limited	100	credit
Sharma Supplies	75	debit

You are to:

(a) Prepare a rent receivable control account for June 2004 from the details above. Show clearly the balance carried down at 30 June 2004, and brought down at 1 July 2004.

(b) Reconcile the rent receivable control account with the total of the subsidiary ledger in the following format:

	£
Rent receivable control account balance as at 30 June 2004	
Total of subsidiary (non-trade debtors) ledger accounts as at 30 June 2004	
Difference	

(c) If there is a difference calculated in (b) above, what do you think might have caused it?

21 INITIAL TRIAL BALANCE AND CORRECTION OF ERRORS

21.1 The following are the business transactions of Robert Jefferson, a bookshop owner, for the months of January and February 2004:

Transactions for January

2004	
1 Jan	Started in business with capital of £5,000 in the bank
2 Jan	Paid rent on premises £200, by cheque
3 Jan	Bought shop fittings £2,000, by cheque
6 Jan	Bought stock of books £2,500, on credit from Northam Publishers
8 Jan	Book sales £1,200, paid into bank
9 Jan	Book sales £1,000, paid into bank
13 Jan	Bought books £5,000, on credit from Broadheath Books
15 Jan	Book sales £1,500 to Teme School, a cheque being received
17 Jan	Book sales, £1,250, paid into bank
20 Jan	Bought books from Financial Publications £2,500, by cheque
23 Jan	Teme School returned unsuitable books £580, cheque refund sent
30 Jan	Sold books on credit to Wyvern College, £1,095

Transactions for February

2004	
3 Feb	Book sales £2,510, paid into bank
5 Feb	Paid rent on premises £200, by cheque
7 Feb	Bought shop fittings £1,385, by cheque
10 Feb	Book sales £3,875, paid into bank
11 Feb	Sent cheque, £2,500, to Northam Publishers
13 Feb	Bought books £1,290, on credit from Northam Publishers
14 Feb	Sent cheque, £5,000, to Broadheath Books
17 Feb	Book sales £1,745, paid into bank
18 Feb	Wyvern College returned books, £250
21 Feb	Book sales £1,435, paid into bank
24 Feb	Bought books £1,250, on credit from Associated Publishers
28 Feb	Book sales £3,900, paid into bank

You are to:

(a) Record the January transactions in his double-entry accounts. Balance all the accounts that have more than one transaction at 31 January 2004

(b) Draw up a trial balance at 31 January 2004

(c) Record the February transactions in his double-entry accounts. Balance all the accounts that have more than one transaction at 29 February 2004

(d) Draw up a trial balance at 29 February 2004

Notes:

- *Robert Jefferson's book-keeping system comprises a cash book (which has a money column for bank only), a main ledger (which includes purchases ledger and sales ledger control accounts), and subsidiary purchases and sales ledgers*
- *day books are not required*
- *Robert Jefferson is not registered for VAT*

21.2 The book-keeper of Lorna Fox has extracted the following list of balances as at 31 March 2004:

	£
Purchases	96,250
Sales	146,390
Sales returns	8,500
Administration expenses	10,240
Wages	28,980
Telephone	3,020
Interest paid	2,350
Travel expenses	1,045
Premises	125,000
Machinery	30,000
Stock at 1 January 2004	8,240
Debtors	12,150
Bank overdraft	1,050
Cash	150
Creditors	9,619
Value Added Tax (credit balance)	2,876
Loan from bank	20,000
Drawings	9,450
Capital	155,440

You are to:

(a) Produce the trial balance at 31 March 2004.

(b) Take any three debit balances and any three credit balances and explain to a trainee who has just started work with the accounts department why they are listed as such, and what this means to the business.

21.3 The purchase of £20 of stationery has been debited to office equipment account. This is:

(a) an error of original entry

(b) an error of principle

(c) a mispost/error of commission

(d) a reversal of entries

Answer (a) or (b) or (c) or (d)

21.4 A credit purchase of £63 from T Billington has been entered in the accounts as £36. This is:

(a) a reversal of entries

(b) an error of original entry

(c) a compensating error

(d) an error of omission

Answer (a) or (b) or (c) or (d)

21.5 Telephone expenses of £250 paid by cheque have been debited to the bank columns of the cash book and credited to the telephone expenses account. Which of the following entries will correct the error?

	Debit		*Credit*	
(a)	Bank	£250	Telephone expenses	£250
(b)	Telephone expenses	£250	Bank	£250
(c)	Bank	£250	Telephone expenses	£250
	Bank	£250	Telephone expenses	£250
(d)	Telephone expenses	£250	Bank	£250
	Telephone expenses	£250	Bank	£250

Answer (a) or (b) or (c) or (d)

21.6 Fill in the missing words from the following sentences:

(a) "You made an error of .... when you debited the cost of diesel fuel for the van to Vans Account."

(b) "I've had the book-keeper from D Jones Limited on the 'phone concerning the statements of account that we sent out the other day. She says that there is a sales invoice charged that she knows nothing about. I wonder if we have done a .... and it should be for T Jones' account?"

(c) "There is a 'bad figure' on a purchases invoice – we have read it as £35 when it should be £55. It has gone through our accounts wrongly so we have an error of .... to put right."

(d) "Although the trial balance balanced last week, I've since found an error of £100 in the calculation of the balance of sales account. We will need to check the other balances as I think we may have a .... error."

(e) "Who was in charge of that trainee last week? He has entered the payment for the electricity bill on the debit side of the bank and on the credit side of electricity – a .... of ...."

(f) "I found this purchase invoice from last week in amongst the copy letters. As we haven't put it through the accounts we have an error of ...."

21.7 A friend, who is just beginning her studies of book-keeping comments:

- "if the trial balance totals agree it is proof that the book-keeping entries are 100 per cent correct"
- "I wouldn't know where to start looking if the trial balance totals did not agree."

What would you reply to your friend?

21.8 The following list of balances was taken from the accounting records of Len Lewis on 31 August 2004:

	£
Office equipment	18,750
Stock	4,525
Debtors	10,294
Creditors	8,731
Bank overdraft	879
Cash	354
VAT (credit balance)	1,396
Capital	25,000
Drawings	15,391
Sales	175,686
Purchases	97,243
Sales returns	3,604
Purchases returns	2,856
General expenses	64,387

On 3 September 2004 the following errors and omissions were discovered:

- a sales invoice for £400 + VAT had not been entered in the sales day book
- a cheque for £625 from a debtor had not been recorded in the accounts
- Len Lewis had taken drawings of £300 by cheque but no entries had been made in the accounts
- a purchases invoice for £200 + VAT had been entered twice in the purchases day book

You are to: prepare a trial balance for Len Lewis' business at 31 August 2004 after adjusting for the above errors and omissions.

21.9 You have recently taken over writing up the double-entry accounts of B Brick (Builders). You have found a number of errors made by the previous book-keeper as follows:

(a) Credit purchase of goods for £85 from J Stone has not been entered in the accounts

(b) A cheque for £155 received from Roger Williams, a debtor, has been credited to the account of another debtor, William Rogers

(c) Diesel fuel costing £30 has been debited to vehicles account

(d) A credit sale for £154 to T Potter has been entered in the accounts as £145

(e) Both purchases returns account and wages account have been overcast by £100

You are to take each error in turn and:

- state the type of error
- show the correcting journal entry

Notes:

- *the accounting system comprises a main ledger (which includes purchases ledger and sales ledger control accounts), and subsidiary purchases and sales ledgers*
- *VAT is to be ignored*
- *use today's date for the journal entries*

21.10 Tracey Truslove is the book-keeper for Mereford Traders Limited. At 30 June 2004 she is unable to balance the trial balance. The difference, £149 credit, is placed to a suspense account pending further investigation.

The following errors are later found:

(a) Purchases account is undercast by £100.

(b) A cheque for £95 for the purchase of stationery has been recorded in the stationery account as £59.

(c) Rent received of £205 has been debited to both the rent received account and the bank account.

(d) Vehicles expenses of £125 have not been entered in the expenses account.

You are to:

- make journal entries to correct the errors
- show the suspense account after the errors have been corrected

Note: VAT is to be ignored; the corrections are to be made on 9 July 2004.

22 USING THE TRIAL BALANCE

The following background information is common to both Student Activities:

You work as an accounts assistant for 'Hotspot Barbecues'. The company manufactures barbecues and accessories, and sells them to garden centres, country shops, and direct to the public. Hotspot Barbecues is registered for VAT.

Your job in the accounts department is principally concerned with the subsidiary purchases and sales ledgers and also with aspects of the main ledger. Main ledger contains purchases ledger and sales ledger control accounts, which form part of the double-entry. Individual accounts of creditors and debtors are kept in subsidiary ledgers.

22.1 Today is 1 August 2004 and you are working on the subsidiary (purchases) ledger and main ledger sections of the accounting system.

Transactions

The following transactions all took place on 1 August 2004 and have been entered into the relevant books of prime entry as shown below. No entries have yet been made into the ledger system. The VAT rate is 17.5%.

PURCHASES DAY BOOK

Date 2004	Details	Invoice No	Total £	VAT £	Net £
1 Aug	Reade Manufacturing	794	1,175	175	1,000
1 Aug	Reed Supplies Ltd	201	1,645	245	1,400
1 Aug	Bourne Limited	387	1,880	280	1,600
1 Aug	Eveshore Services	924	2,350	350	2,000
	TOTALS		7,050	1,050	6,000

PURCHASES RETURNS DAY BOOK

Date 2004	Details	Credit Note No	Total £	VAT £	Net £
1 Aug	Eveshore Services	CN 68	235	35	200
1 Aug	Reed Supplies Ltd	CN 32	517	77	440
	TOTALS		752	112	640

CASH BOOK

Date 2004	Details	Discount Allowed	Bank £	Date 2004	Details	Discount Received	Bank £
1 Aug	Balance b/d		4,200	1 Aug	Bourne Limited		2,500
1 Aug	Rent received		500	1 Aug	Reade Manufacturing	75	2,925
1 Aug	Balance c/d		770	1 Aug	Bank charges		45
			5,470			75	5,470

Balances to be inserted in ledger accounts

The following balances are relevant to you at the start of the day on 1 August 2004:

	£
Credit suppliers:	
Bourne Limited	3,840
Eveshore Services	2,330
Reade Manufacturing	3,000
Reed Supplies Limited	3,690
Purchases ledger control	12,860
Purchases	197,384
Purchases returns	2,590
Discount received	710
Rent received	3,250
Bank charges	335
VAT (credit balance)	3,980

Balances to be transferred to trial balance

	£
Premises	125,000
Machinery	30,000
Vehicles	28,200
Stock	15,590
Cash	200
Sales ledger control	35,390
Capital	120,000
Sales	376,332
Sales returns	3,640
Discount allowed	845
Wages and salaries	68,140
Electricity	5,260
Bad debts written off	434
Vehicle expenses	3,174
Rates paid	1,930

Task 1.1 Enter the opening balances listed on the previous page (111) into the following accounts given on the next four pages (113 - 116):

Subsidiary (purchases) ledger

Bourne Limited
Eveshore Services
Reade Manufacturing
Reed Supplies Limited

Main ledger

Purchases ledger control
Purchases
Purchases returns
Discount received
Rent received
Bank charges
VAT

Task 1.2 From the day books and cash book shown on pages 110 and 111 make the relevant entries in the accounts in the subsidiary (purchases) ledger and the main ledger.

Task 1.3 Balance the accounts showing clearly the balances carried down at 1 August 2004 (closing balance).

Task 1.4 Now that you have closed the above accounts, show clearly the balance brought down at 2 August 2004 (opening balance). Demonstrate a reconciliation of the balance of purchases ledger control account with the subsidiary accounts.

Task 1.5 Transfer the balances calculated in task 1.3, and from the cash book, to the trial balance shown on page 116.

Task 1.6 Transfer the remaining balances shown at the top of page 112 to the trial balance and total each column. The debit column and credit column totals should be the same.

Tasks 1.1, 1.2, 1.3 and 1.4

SUBSIDIARY (PURCHASES) LEDGER

Bourne Limited

Date	Details	Amount £	Date	Details	Amount £

Eveshore Services

Date	Details	Amount £	Date	Details	Amount £

Reade Manufacturing

Date	Details	Amount £	Date	Details	Amount £

SUBSIDIARY (PURCHASES) LEDGER

Reed Supplies Limited

Date	Details	Amount £	Date	Details	Amount £

Reconciliation of purchases ledger control account

	1 Aug 2004 £	2 Aug 2004 £
Bourne Limited		
Eveshore Services		
Reade Manufacturing		
Reed Supplies Limited		
Purchases ledger control account (see below)		

MAIN LEDGER

Purchases ledger control

Date	Details	Amount £	Date	Details	Amount £

Purchases

Date	Details	Amount £	Date	Details	Amount £

MAIN LEDGER

Purchases returns

Date	Details	Amount £	Date	Details	Amount £

Discount received

Date	Details	Amount £	Date	Details	Amount £

Rent received

Date	Details	Amount £	Date	Details	Amount £

Bank charges

Date	Details	Amount £	Date	Details	Amount £

MAIN LEDGER

VAT

Date	Details	Amount £	Date	Details	Amount £

Tasks 1.5 and 1.6

TRIAL BALANCE AS AT 1 AUGUST 2004

	Debit £	Credit £
Premises	....	....
Machinery	....	....
Vehicles	....	....
Stock	....	....
Bank	....	....
Cash	....	....
Sales ledger control	....	....
Capital	....	....
Sales	....	....
Sales returns	....	....
Discount allowed	....	....
Wages and salaries	....	....
Electricity	....	....
Bad debts written off	....	....
Vehicle expenses	....	....
Rates paid	....	....
Purchases ledger control	....	....
Purchases	....	....
Purchases returns	....	....
Discount received	....	....
Rent received	....	....
Bank charges	....	....
VAT	....	....
TOTAL	....	....

22.2 Today is 2 August 2004 and you are working on the main ledger and subsidiary (sales) ledger sections of the accounting system.

Transactions

The following transactions all took place on 2 August 2004 and have been entered into the relevant books of prime entry as shown below. No entries have yet been made into the ledger system. The VAT rate is 17.5%.

SALES DAY BOOK

Date 2004	Details	Invoice No	Total £	VAT £	Net £
2 Aug	Charlton Home Furnishings	504	940	140	800
2 Aug	Tauntone Country Store	505	1,175	175	1,000
2 Aug	A-Z Garden Centre	506	1,410	210	1,200
2 Aug	Charlton Home Furnishings	507	470	70	400
	TOTALS		3,995	595	3,400

SALES RETURNS DAY BOOK

Date 2004	Details	Credit Note No	Total £	VAT £	Net £
2 Aug	A-Z Garden Centre	CN 63	188	28	160
2 Aug	Tauntone Country Store	CN 64	329	49	280
	TOTALS		517	77	440

CASH BOOK

Date 2004	Details	Discount Allowed	Bank £	Date 2004	Details	Discount Received	Bank £
2 Aug	Charlton Home Furnishings	60	2,340	2 Aug	Balance b/d		770
2 Aug	A-Z Garden Centre		1,000	2 Aug	Wages and salaries		3,227
2 Aug	Balance c/d		657				
		60	3,997				3,997

Balances to be inserted in ledger accounts

The following balances are relevant to you at the start of the day on 2 August 2004:

	£
Credit customers:	
A-Z Garden Centre	2,052
Charlton Home Furnishings	12,400
Ralph's Gardens	141
Tauntone Country Store	20,797
Sales ledger control	35,390
Sales	376,332
Sales returns	3,640
Discount allowed	845
Vehicles	28,200
Vehicle expenses	3,174
Wages and salaries	68,140
VAT (credit balance)	3,042
Bad debts written off	434

Journal entries

The accounts supervisor asks you to make entries in the journal and the double-entry accounts for the following:

- the subsidiary (sales) ledger account balance in the name of Ralph's Gardens is to be written off as a bad debt; you are told that VAT relief is available on this debt
- an amount of £200 + VAT for vehicle expenses was debited to vehicles account in error on 26 July 2004

Balances to be transferred to trial balance

	£
Premises	125,000
Machinery	30,000
Stock	15,590
Cash	200
Capital	120,000
Electricity	5,260
Rates paid	1,930
Purchases ledger control	13,658
Purchases	203,384
Purchases returns	3,230
Discount received	785
Rent received	3,750
Bank charges	380

Task 2.1 Enter the opening balances listed on the previous page (118) into the following accounts given on the next four pages (120 - 123):

Subsidiary (sales) ledger

A-Z Garden Centre

Charlton Home Furnishings

Ralph's Gardens

Tauntone Country Store

Main ledger

Sales ledger control

Sales

Sales returns

Discount allowed

Vehicles

Vehicle expenses

Wages and salaries

VAT

Bad debts written off

Task 2.2

- From the day books and cash book shown on page 117 make the relevant entries in the accounts in the subsidiary (sales) ledger and the main ledger.
- Record the entries in the journal on page 123 (narratives are not required) for the transactions mentioned by the accounts supervisor and then enter the transactions into the relevant accounts.

Task 2.3 Balance the accounts showing clearly the balances carried down at 2 August 2004 (closing balance).

Task 2.4 Now that you have closed the above accounts, show clearly the balance brought down at 3 August 2004 (opening balance). Demonstrate a reconciliation of sales ledger control account with the subsidiary accounts.

Task 2.5 Transfer the balances calculated in task 2.3, and from the cash book, to the trial balance shown on page 124.

Task 2.6 Transfer the remaining balances shown at the bottom of page 118 to the trial balance and total each column. The debit column and credit column totals should be the same.

Tasks 2.1, 2.2, 2.3 and 2.4

SUBSIDIARY (SALES) LEDGER

A-Z Garden Centre

Date	Details	Amount £	Date	Details	Amount £

Charlton Home Furnishings

Date	Details	Amount £	Date	Details	Amount £

Ralph's Gardens

Date	Details	Amount £	Date	Details	Amount £

Tauntone Country Store

Date	Details	Amount £	Date	Details	Amount £

Reconciliation of sales ledger control account

	2 Aug 2004	3 Aug 2004
	£	£
A-Z Garden Centre		
Charlton Home Furnishings		
Ralph's Gardens		
Tauntone Country Store		
Sales ledger control account (see below)		

MAIN LEDGER

Sales ledger control

Date	Details	Amount £	Date	Details	Amount £

Sales

Date	Details	Amount £	Date	Details	Amount £

Sales returns

Date	Details	Amount £	Date	Details	Amount £

MAIN LEDGER

Discount allowed

Date	Details	Amount £	Date	Details	Amount £

Vehicles

Date	Details	Amount £	Date	Details	Amount £

Vehicle expenses

Date	Details	Amount £	Date	Details	Amount £

Wages and salaries

Date	Details	Amount £	Date	Details	Amount £

MAIN LEDGER

VAT

Date	Details	Amount £	Date	Details	Amount £

Bad debts written off

Date	Details	Amount £	Date	Details	Amount £

JOURNAL

Date	*Details*	*Debit*	*Credit*

Tasks 2.5 and 2.6

TRIAL BALANCE AS AT 1 AUGUST 2004

	Debit	Credit
	£	£
Premises	....	....
Machinery	....	....
Vehicles	....	....
Stock	....	....
Bank	....	....
Cash	....	....
Sales ledger control	....	....
Capital	....	....
Sales	....	....
Sales returns	....	....
Discount allowed	....	....
Wages and salaries	....	....
Electricity	....	....
Bad debts written off	....	....
Vehicle expenses	....	....
Rates paid	....	....
Purchases ledger control	....	....
Purchases	....	....
Purchases returns	....	....
Discount received	....	....
Rent received	....	....
Bank charges	....	....
VAT	....	....
TOTAL	....	....

23 INFORMATION FOR MANAGEMENT CONTROL

23.1 In the first list below, five items of information are shown, labelled A to E. These are examples of the kind of information which managers of a business might find useful. In the second list below, six possible management tasks are shown, labelled (i) to (vi).

For each of the six management tasks, list the items of information from the first list, A to E, which managers may find useful for that task. There may be more than one item for each task and the items may be used more than once.

A Rates of pay for different grades of labour

B Sales forecasts for a product for the next year at different selling prices

C The total cost of repairs to machinery in the last year

D Estimated prices of raw materials for the next year

E The amount of time lost during the last year due to machine breakdowns

(i) Deciding on selling prices for products in the future

(ii) Budgeting for the cost of production for the next year

(iii) Checking monthly totals of wages

(iv) Deciding whether to scrap old machines and buy new ones

(v) Preparing a budget for the next quarter, to make sure sufficient cash is available when needed

(vi) Finding ways to reduce costs within the business.

23.2 For each of the management tasks (i) to (vi) in Activity 23.1 (above), state which of the following functions of management would best describe that task:

Decision-making

Planning

Control

23.3 Which of the phrases below describe features of financial accounting and which describe features of management accounting?

(a) reports relating to what has happened in the past

(b) may be required by law

(c) gives estimates of costs and income for the future

(d) may be made public

(e) gives up-to-date reports which can be used for controlling the business

(f) is used by people outside the business

(g) is designed to meet requirements of people inside the business

(h) shows details of the costs of materials, labour and expenses

(i) records accurate amounts, not estimates

23.4 A friend of yours, Rob Willis, started his own business several years ago, making small toys from moulded plastics. The business has expanded rapidly and now employs 8 production workers, 4 people in selling and distribution and 3 office workers. A book-keeper records all the business transactions and, at the end of the financial year, the financial accounts are prepared by an accountant. Up to now, Rob Willis has managed the business fairly successfully, making decisions on a day-to-day basis. So that he can improve his management skills he asks your advice about making use of management accounting information.

Write a note to Rob Willis explaining how management accounting differs from financial accounting, and suggesting ways in which management accounting information might help him in managing his business.

23.5 The following are items of expenditure incurred in a company which manufactures clothing. Write them in three columns, headed 'Materials costs', 'Labour costs' and 'Expenses'.

(a) Premium for the insurance of buildings

(b) Salaries of the office staff

(c) The cost of zip fasteners

(d) The cost of electricity

(e) Wages of storekeepers

(f) Overtime payments for machinists

(g) The cost of a consignment of blue denim

(h) The cost of preprinted stationery

(i) The cost of television advertising

(j) The cost of cones of thread

(k) Road fund licences for vehicles

(l) The canteen chef's wages

23.6 Suggest likely cost centres or profit centres for each of the following:

A theatre in a provincial town, where touring productions are staged. The theatre has a bar and a confectionery counter. Ticket sales are dealt with by the theatre's own box office, and the plays are advertised locally.

A garage, which sells both new and used cars of two different makes. Cars are also repaired, serviced and valeted.

23.7 You work for Gold and Partners, Chartered Accountants, who have three offices in neighbouring districts in the suburbs of London. The Senior Partner, Lawrence Gold, sent the following memo to your line manager, Marie McCall. You have been asked to extract and prepare the information requested in the memo. The offices are referred to as R, S and T. They are all of similar size.

MEMORANDUM

To: M. McCall

From: L. Gold

Date: 26 October 2004

Subject: Annual Review: year ended 30.9.04

I am in the process of reviewing the firm's figures for the year ended 30 September and require the following:

- Income totals for each of the three offices.
- Costs for each of the three offices, broken down into materials, labour and expenses.
- Profit and Return on Investment calculated for each office separately.

Please supply these as soon as possible.

You extract the following information from the records:

Income for the year ended 30 September 2004:

Office R:	£950,000
Office S:	£869,000
Office T:	£1,195,500

Materials costs for the year ended 30 September 2004:

Office R:	£75,000
Office S:	£7,000
Office T:	£8,400

Labour costs for the year ended 30 September 2004:

Office R:	£650,000
Office S:	£550,000
Office T:	£730,000

Expenses for the year ended 30 September 2004:

Office R:	£82,500
Office S:	£69,000
Office T:	£89,100

The amount of money invested in each office at 30 September 2004 is as follows:

Office R:	£750,000
Office S:	£900,000
Office T:	£1,150,000

Which of these amounts appears to be incorrect and should be queried with Marie McCall?

Marie McCall investigates your query and agrees that an error has been made. The correct figure is £7,500, which you should use. She suggests that you write out of all the above information in columns, with one column for the narrative and one for each Office (see the format below). When you have calculated the profit for each office and the return on investment, these can also be entered in the columns, in order to present the information clearly for Lawrence Gold.

	Office R (£)	Office S (£)	Office T (£)
Materials			
Labour			
Expenses			
TOTAL COSTS			
Income			
PROFIT			
Money invested			
Return on Investment (%)			

23.8 In your summer holiday, you are doing some voluntary work in the office of a charity. The charity raises money through Members' Subscriptions, Shops, Street Collections and Donations and a Christmas Mail Order Catalogue. Much of the work done for the charity is unpaid, but there is a certain amount of paid work in essential administration. There are also some costs of materials and expenses which are not donated. The Christmas Mail Order has costs similar to businesses. The chief administrator of the charity has asked you to draw up a table, as follows:

YEAR ENDED 31.12.2004	Street Collections and Donations (£)	Shops (£)	Christmas Mail Order (£)	Members' Subscriptions (£)
Materials				
Labour				
Expenses				
TOTAL COSTS				
Income				
Surplus of Income over total costs (see Note 1)				
Surplus as a percentage of Income (Note 2)				

Note 1: Surplus = Income – total costs, similar to profit for a business

Note 2: To calculate the surplus as a percentage of income, the formula is:

$$\frac{SURPLUS}{INCOME} \times 100\%$$

You are to extract the following information for the year from the records and complete the table.

Christmas Mail Order

Income from sales was £375,300.

Costs were: materials £260,000, labour £46,000, expenses £13,000

Street Collections and Donations

Income was £12,650.

Costs were: materials £2,500, labour £3,000, expenses £1,800

Shops

Income was £78,600.

Costs were: materials £8,300, labour £21,000, expenses £5,700

Members' Subscriptions

Income was £11,200

Costs were: Materials £900, labour £3,000, expenses £1,800

23.9 In your everyday life there are almost certainly a number of coding systems which you use, or systems which apply codes to you personally or to your household. For example, the system of Post Codes, which in the UK consist of combinations of letters and numbers. Some coding systems use numbers only and some letters only.

Identify at least *three* coding systems which you use or which are applied to you in your everyday life. State whether the codes are made up of letters or numbers or combinations of both. Provide examples of the codes used within each system.

23.10 The following is an extract from the coding reference manual for a company which processes sugar beet. The sugar which is produced is then packed for distribution.

Extract from list of cost centre codes:

Beet preparation	010
Processing	020
Packing	030
Administration	040
Quality control	050
Distribution	060

Extract from list of expenditure codes:

Sugar beet	1010
Stationery	1050
Machine operators' wages	2010
Supervisory wages	2040
Drivers' wages	2050
Heating and lighting	3020
Power for machinery	3030
Telephone	3040

Each item of expenditure is to be coded with the appropriate cost centre code, followed by the expenditure code, eg Distribution drivers' wages would be coded 060 2050.

Determine the codes for the following in this way (ignore VAT):

(a) Wages paid to machine operators in the processing department

(b) Cost of telephone calls made by the administration department

(c) Cost of electricity used for heating the packing department

(d) Cost of stationery used in the administration department

(e) Wages of the supervisor in the preparation department

(f) Cost of a consignment of beet to be charged to the preparation department

(g) Cost of power used to run the processing machines

(h) Cost of stationery used by the quality control inspectors

24 PRESENTING AND COMPARING MANAGEMENT INFORMATION

24.1 You are working in the accounts department of a company which manufactures electrical goods in several factories and you are passed the following memorandum

> ***MEMORANDUM***
>
> To: Accounts dept.
> From: Production Manager, East Region
> Date: 28 August 2004
> Subject: Costing
>
> I need some information for sending in a report to Head Office, as follows:
>
> - materials costs for last month in the two East Region factories
> - labour costs as above, showing basic and overtime for different grades of production employees.
>
> I need this by the end of the week, please.

List and explain briefly the factors you would have to bear in mind when preparing a reply to this memorandum.

24.2 You have just started work in a small firm which designs and makes curtains to customers' requirements. The curtains are delivered and hung for the clients. You have been asked to sort out some information and present it in a table for the owner, who wants to review how prices are set.

The figures have been jotted down in a notebook by the workshop supervisor, as shown below. Omitting unnecessary text, show the financial information in columns (a column for each job). The costs should be split into Materials, Labour and Expenses. The total cost and the selling price for each job should also be shown.

NOTES

22/8/04 Mrs Johnston:

Measure/design visit (Jane), wages £20;

Lux/Olive Green fabric 22m @ £16.50 per metre and Olive green lining needed 20m @ £7.40 per metre.

Tapes etc £15

Labour: Cutting: 2 hrs at £10 per hr, Making 7 hrs @ £8 per hr

continued on next page

Return visit (Jane and Pete), wages £30.

General expenses £50.

Total cost £702, selling Price £840.

28/8/04 Mr and Mrs Wright:

Measure/design (Paul), wages £20.

Require 10m @ £19.50 per m, (Arcadia check, blue/beige).

Plus 8m @ £18.00 per m, (Arcadia plain blue) and lining 18m @ £7.40 (mid-blue).

Tapes etc £14, Tiebacks (twist, ref 65b) £32.

Labour: Cutting 2 hrs @ £10 per hr, Making 8 hrs @ £8 per hr.

Return visit (Paul and Jane) wages £30.

General expenses, £40.

Total cost £692.20, selling price £830.

31/8/04 Timms and Co (Board Room):

Measure/design visit (Paul), wages £20.

Require 14m @ £27.50 (old gold, ref v131) plus lining 14m @ £7.40 (gold).

Labour: Cutting 1.5 hrs @ £10 per hr, Making 8 hrs @ £8 per hr.

Tapes, pelmet backing, braid (lt. Bronze), etc £38.

Return visit (Pete and Paul), wages £30.

General expenses, £50.

Total cost £705.60, selling price £850.

24.3 Greens Garden Services is a firm which carries out landscaping, grass-cutting and general garden work. You have the following information:

Greens Garden Services: Monthly Income in £.												
Year	Jan	Feb	Mar	Apr	May	June	July	Aug	Sept	Oct	Nov	Dec
2004	900	2100	3000	3000	4200	3300	4350	4200	4200	2100	900	600
2005	300	2400	3250	3750	4100	4200	4500	3600	4000	2000	1500	1500

Prepare a table to show the monthly cumulative totals of Greens Garden Services income for each of the years 2004 and 2005.

24.4 The following forecasts of monthly sales income for the year 2004 were made by the manager of a large public house.

Forecast Sales Income: The Red Lion. Monthly forecast, year 2004												
	Jan	Feb	Mar	Apr	May	June	July	Aug	Sept	Oct	Nov	Dec
£	4000	4000	4500	4500	4500	5000	5000	5500	4500	4000	3500	5000

Actual figures for sales income for the first eight months are now available:

Actual Sales Income: The Red Lion. Monthly Income, year 2004												
	Jan	Feb	Mar	Apr	May	June	July	Aug	Sept	Oct	Nov	Dec
£	3600	3900	4100	4200	4800	5200	4800	5700				

Prepare a table to allow comparison of actual sales income of The Red Lion with the forecast, for corresponding months and for cumulative totals. Complete the table as far as possible.

24.5 You work part-time in the office of a theatre in a city in the west of England. The theatre manager, Kate Leith, has left a note on your desk as follows:

> 3/10/05
>
> From: Kate Leith
>
> Kevin: could you please find out the following for me:
>
> - Total costs for the quarter July-Sept inclusive this year
> - Forecast total cost figure for the same quarter this year
> - Total cost figure for the corresponding quarter last year

You look up the information needed to answer these questions, and find the following table:

Albion Theatre: Quarterly Costs			
All in £000s	**Actual Year 2004**	**Forecast Year 2005**	**Actual Year 2005**
Jan-Mar	135	150	153
Apr-June	151	165	169
July-Sept	144	165	172
Oct-Dec	139	160	

Set out a suitable reply to the note from Kate Leith. What method would you use to give the reply?

24.6 The Albion Theatre costs for the quarter October to December 2005 amount to £156,000. Enter this figure in the table. Then deduct the 2005 actual figures from the forecast figures and complete the right hand column to show the differences. Indicate whether the difference is a '+' difference or '–' difference. Finally, total each column for the year.

Albion Theatre Quarterly Costs				
All in £000s	**Actual Year 2004**	**Forecast Year 2005**	**Actual Year 2005**	**Difference + or – Year 2005**
Jan-Mar	135	150	153	
Apr-June	151	165	169	
July-Sept	144	165	172	
Oct-Dec	139	160		
TOTAL				

24.7 You work in the accounts office of a garage, which has a repairs and servicing department as well as a sales department. You have been asked to complete the following Standard Cost Report:

STANDARD COST REPORT - Fox Motors **Department:** Repairs and Servicing **Period:** Week commencing 6 Nov 2004			
	Forecast Cost (£)	**Actual Cost (£)**	**Difference (£) + or -**
MATERIALS	6,000	5,380	
LABOUR	1,200		
EXPENSES	1,000		
TOTAL			

You have to ask your supervisor for the actual labour and expenses and you are told that these are £1,350 for labour and £875 for expenses.

Complete the report as requested by completing the difference column and the totals boxes.

24.8 You work as assistant to the management accountant in Floristry Supplies Ltd, a company which sells fresh flowers on a wholesale basis. You are asked to complete as far as possible the following Comparative Sales Report. Percentages should be rounded to one decimal place.

SALES BUDGETARY CONTROL REPORT – FLORISTRY SUPPLIES LTD

Date: *August 2004*

	Sales 2003 (monthly) £000s	**Sales 2004 (monthly) £000s**	**Difference £000s (+ or –)**	**Percentage difference (+ or –)**
January	130	126		
February	200	211		
March	180	169		
April	170	167		
May	150	161		
June	160	164		
July	160	155		
August	150	148		
September	150			
October	150			
November	160			
December	200			
TOTAL	1,960			

24.9 You work as assistant to the management accountant in Top Taste Ltd, a company which manufactures a number of brands of biscuits. You are asked to complete the following Monthly Product Sales Report, adding in the missing figures, the difference and the percentage difference (round the percentage to one decimal place).

PRODUCT SALES REPORT – TOP TASTE LTD

Date: *March 2005*

Product Code	Forecast Sales £000s	Actual Sales £000s	Actual–Forecast (+ or –) £000s	Percentage difference
B110	55	58		
B123	60	57		
B147	50	52		
C342	25			
C355	25			
C369	30			
C371	30			
D588	45	49		
D590	40	39		
TOTAL				

You have to find out the figures for four of the products. From department C, you obtain the following information:

March 2005 Actual Sales, Department C:

Product Code C342 £27,000

Product Code C355 £24,000

Product Code C369 £28,000

Product Code C371 £33,000

Enter these missing Sales figures in the report and complete the rest of the table.

24.10 In the offices of Top Taste Ltd, there have recently been several problems caused by the unauthorised use of confidential information. You have therefore decided that staff should be reminded about the correct procedures for confidential items. You are planning to put a poster on the wall in each office, showing "The Do's and Don'ts for Confidential Info".

List and explain briefly the main points which you would highlight on the poster.

Unit 1
Recording income and receipts

Simulation 1
Compuware.com

NVQ Element coverage

1.1 process documents relating to goods and services supplied

1.2 process receipts

Scenario and contents

This Simulation is based on Compuware.com Limited, a company which supplies computers, accessories and software to businesses and to the general public. The company sells on credit to its business customers and also operates a shop where the public can make purchases.

The tasks in the Simulation include:

- preparation and checking of customer invoices from orders received
- preparation and checking of credit notes in reply to requests for credit
- recording credit transactions in the appropriate accounting records
- preparing statements of account to be sent to customers
- checking cheques, debit/credit card and cash receipts and entering them in the accounting records
- preparing paying-in documents

Suggested time allocation: three hours plus fifteen minutes reading time

SIMULATION 1
COMPUWARE.COM

SITUATION

You work in the Accounts Department of Compuware.com, a company which sells computers, accessories and software to businesses and to the general public. The business is located on a business park. The address is Compuware.com Limited, Unit 14 Monkwood Estate, Witley Green, MR3 6TH.

Your work is varied and involves processing orders received from businesses who buy on credit, dealing with the cheque, credit/debit card and cash receipts which come from sales over the shop counter on the premises, and keeping the accounting records up-to-date. Internal sales orders must be authorised by Mark Allen, Sales Administrator. Prepared invoices and credit notes should be passed to the Accounts Supervisor, Ivor Pound, for authorisation.

GOODS SUPPLIED TO CUSTOMERS ON CREDIT

Compuware.com sells on credit to a number of business customers. It gives varying trade discounts to regular customers and offers, on request, a settlement discount of 2.5% for payment of invoices within 14 days of issue. An extract from the customer database is shown below.

Compuware.com gives 30 days credit on its invoices and sends out monthly statements of account. It is company policy to chase up invoices which have not been settled in the month following issue – ie in March it will chase up invoices issued in January and earlier.

Compuware.com is registered for VAT and charges VAT at the current rate on all sales.

An extract from the customer database is shown below.

Compuware.com Customer database (extract)

customer details	account no.	trade discount	credit limit £	balance £ (1 June 2004)
Harpney Ltd 12 Gretarex Road, Chelnor, MR1 6YT	3412	10%	10,000	8,560.00
Brinkman & Co Unit 2 Freshwater Estate, Grantley, GR4 6FG	3520	15%	25,000	18,960.50
King Designs Ltd 45 High Road, Hexworth, HW3 6VB	3340	10%	10,000	3,450.00
D Shaw & Partners Equity House, The Square, Pithwick, PW2 7FG	3401	20%	40,000	25,500.60
Star Insurance Brokers 7 Broad Street, Mereford, MR1 7CF	3521	15%	30,000	1,960.80
Hellrose Associates 8 The Terrace, Malpeck, HR6 8HG	3470	10%	10,000	12,750.70

COUNTER SALES

Compuware.com operates a retail shop at its premises and sells to members of the public on a cash basis – ie it accepts cash, cheques and debit/credit card payments. There are two EFTPOS tills in use. At the end of each day the debit card and credit card payment totals are automatically sent via computer link to Compuware's bank account. The total of the cash and cheque receipts is recorded by the senior cashier on a Receipts Summary which is used by you on a daily basis to prepare a bank paying-in slip.

BANKING DETAILS

Compuware.com has a business account with Western Bank Plc at its Witley Green branch.

PRODUCTS

Compuware.com sells a wide range of computers, accessories and software. An extract from its catalogue is shown below.

Compuware.com Product catalogue (extract)

code	product	unit	price £ (excluding VAT)
101008	Zap3 desktop computer	each	650.00
101009	Zap4 desktop computer	each	750.00
101010	Zap5 desktop computer	each	950.00
101020	Mercury laptop computer	each	1,150.00
101045	Digiviz digital camera	each	695.00
102007	Zap65 CD writer	each	495.00
103007	Zap CD diskpack (10 CDs in a box)	box	49.50
103008	Zap DVD diskpack (10 DVDs in a box)	box	65.50
150101	Macrohard 'The Business' software	each	400.00
150102	Adept 'Photomake' software	each	450.00
150109	Querk 'Page Manager' software	each	600.00
150110	Wizbooks accounting software	each	900.00

ACCOUNTING RECORDS

Compuware.com records sales invoices in a sales day book, and credit notes issued in a sales returns day book. A manual system of double-entry book-keeping is used, with a cash book and a main (general) ledger. The main ledger includes a control account for debtors, with customer accounts contained in a subsidiary (sales) ledger.

TASKS

PART 1: DEALING WITH CREDIT SALES

1 Refer to the 4 purchase orders and 2 sales orders on pages 142 to 144, the price list on page 139 and the customer details on page 138.

Two of the orders will need referring to Ivor Pound, the Accounts Supervisor. Decide which orders these are and write a memo (see page 145) to your supervisor explaining the problem.

The date is 4 June 2004

2 Complete the four sales invoices on pages 146 to 149.

Remember to apply the correct trade discount in all cases and allow settlement discount when it is requested by a customer.

VAT is chargeable at the current rate on all sales.

The date is 4 June 2004

3 Enter the four sales invoices from task 2 (assuming they have been authorised) into the sales day book on page 165.

Total the sales day book and record the accounting entries in the main (general) ledger and subsidiary (sales) ledger accounts on pages 166 to 168. Note: opening balances are shown on these accounts where appropriate.

4 On 12 June 2004 you receive the three requests for credit shown on pages 150 to 152 (two emails and a returns note).

You investigate the delivery to D Shaw and Partners and find that the goods were delivered to the correct address of D Shaw and Partners on 6 June. Your carrier (Puma Parcels) faxes you a copy of the signed delivery note shown on page 152.

You refer the matter to your supervisor Ivor Pound and he asks you to:

(a) complete the two credit notes (on pages 153 and 154) for Star Insurance and King Designs

(b) draft a letter to D Shaw and Partners (page 155) for Mr Pound's signature explaining that credit cannot be given at present because the goods have been delivered; the letter should attach a copy of the fax showing the signature of R Bradshaw who accepted the parcel

5 Enter the two sales credit notes from task 4 (assuming they have been authorised) into the sales returns day book on page 165.

Total the sales returns day book and record the accounting entries in the main (general) ledger and subsidiary (sales) ledger accounts on pages 166 to 168.

6 In your in-tray on 12 June 2004 are five cheques received from customers in respect of outstanding accounts (see pages 156-157). You are to

(a) Check the cheques for any technical irregularities. Note any problems with the cheques and action required on page 158.

(b) Refer to the extract from the aged debtors analysis on page 157. Write a letter to Hellrose Associates in response to their query on their remittance advice. Point out that their account is overdue according to the company's credit terms. You may sign the letter in your own name (see page 159).

7 Record in the cash book (page 167) the valid cheques received from customers – the cheques were banked on 12 June 2004 – and make the entries in the main (general) ledger and subsidiary (sales) ledger accounts on pages 166 to 168.

8 At the end of the month you prepare statements for your credit customers. Prepare the statements (page 160) for Star Insurance and King Designs and date them 30 June 2004. Use the opening balance shown on the customer database (page 138) and remember to include any payments received.

PART 2: DEALING WITH CASH SALES

The Compuware.com shop has two EFTPOS tills operating during the working day. Both tills accept cash, cheques and debit/credit card payments. At the end of each day the debit card and credit card payment totals are automatically sent via computer link to Compuware's bank account and are recorded on a printout from each till.

At the end of each day, the cashiers Jade Mason and Rashid Singh count up the cash and add up the cheques. The total of the cash, cheques, debit and credit card sales are recorded on a till summary for each till. The amounts that are to be paid into the bank (the cash and cheques) are then transferred to a Bank Summary Sheet which is used as the basis for the preparation of a bank paying-in slip.

9 Complete the two till summaries for 4 June 2004 on pages 161 and 162 from the information given.

10 Complete the Bank Summary Sheet on page 163 from the two till summaries.

11 Complete the bank paying-in slip on page 164. It will be paid in on 5 June 2004. List the cheques on the reverse of the paying-in slip.

12 Enter the amount of the till receipts into the cash book and sales account on pages 167 and 166.

Note: record separate figures in the accounts for the amount banked, debit card receipts, and credit card receipts

ANSWER PAGES

Harpney Limited
12 Gretarex Road
Chelnor
MR1 6YT
01908 672561
VAT REG GB 0745 8383 66

PURCHASE ORDER

Compuware.com Limited
Unit 14 Monkwood Estate
Witley Green
MR3 6TH

purchase order no **355345**
date **30 05 04**

product code	quantity	description
1001008	**1**	**Zap4 desktop computer @ £750**

AUTHORISED signature...date..........................

Brinkman & Co
Unit 2 Freshwater Estate,
Grantley, GR4 6FG
01203 987562
VAT REG GB 0988 8644 12

PURCHASE ORDER

Compuware.com Limited
Unit 14 Monkwood Estate
Witley Green
MR3 6TH

purchase order no **92342**
date **29 05 04**

product code	quantity	description
1001008	**1**	**Zap3 desktop computer @ £650** **Please allow 2.5% cash discount as normal**

AUTHORISED signature *D Brinkman* date *29/05/04*

COMPUWARE.COM LIMITED

Unit 14, Monkwood Estate, Witley Green, MR3 6TH
Tel 01908 765311 Fax 01908 765953 Email
compuware@goblin.com
VAT Reg GB 0456 1007 19

Sales Order

King Designs Limited
45 High Road
Hexworth
HW3 6VB

sales order no 24342
date 03 06 04

product code	quantity	description
101045	1	Digiviz digital camera @ £695

AUTHORISED signature *Mark Allen* date *03/06/04*

COMPUWARE.COM LIMITED

Unit 14, Monkwood Estate, Witley Green, MR3 6TH
Tel 01908 765311 Fax 01908 765953 Email
compuware@goblin.com
VAT Reg GB 0456 1007 19

Sales Order

D Shaw & Partners
Equity House
The Square
Pithwick PW2 7FG

sales order no 24343
date 03 06 04

product code	quantity	description
102007	1	Zap65 CD writer @ £495
103007	1 box of 10	Zap CD diskpack @ £49.50

AUTHORISED signature *Mark Allen* date *03/06/04*

***Note**: a Sales Order is an internal document completed by a business when it receives an order without a supporting purchase order – for example an order received by telephone. The Sales Order fulfils the same function as a Purchase Order and will need internal authorisation.*

Star Insurance Brokers
7 Broad Street
Mereford
MR1 7CF
01908 333391
VAT REG GB 2873 8276 34

PURCHASE ORDER

Compuware.com Limited
Unit 14 Monkwood Estate
Witley Green
MR3 6TH

purchase order no **2444**
date **28 05 04**

product code	quantity	description
150109	1	Querk Page Manager @ £600
150102	1	Adept Photomake @ £450
103007	2 boxes	Zap CD diskpack @ £49.50 each

AUTHORISED signature *H Taylor* date *28/05/04*

Hellrose Associates
8, The Terrace
Malpeck
HR6 8HG
01303 542863
VAT REG GB 0911 8633 11

PURCHASE ORDER

Compuware.com Limited
Unit 14 Monkwood Estate
Witley Green
MR3 6TH

purchase order no **9653**
date **29 05 04**

product code	quantity	description
1001008	2	Zap3 desktop computers @ £650 each

AUTHORISED signature *J Rose* date *29/05/04*

MEMORANDUM

To

From

Date

Subject

INVOICE

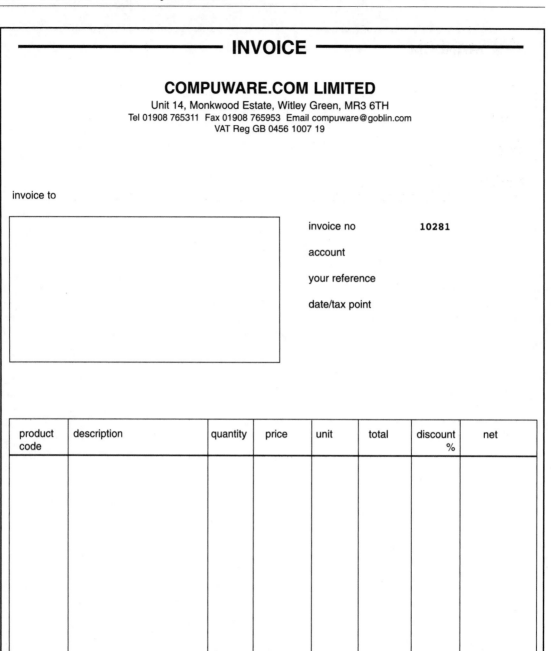

COMPUWARE.COM LIMITED

Unit 14, Monkwood Estate, Witley Green, MR3 6TH
Tel 01908 765311 Fax 01908 765953 Email compuware@goblin.com
VAT Reg GB 0456 1007 19

invoice to

invoice no **10281**

account

your reference

date/tax point

product code	description	quantity	price	unit	total	discount %	net

goods total	
VAT	
TOTAL	

terms
Net monthly
Carriage paid
E & OE

INVOICE

COMPUWARE.COM LIMITED

Unit 14, Monkwood Estate, Witley Green, MR3 6TH
Tel 01908 765311 Fax 01908 765953 Email compuware@goblin.com
VAT Reg GB 0456 1007 19

invoice to

invoice no **10282**

account

your reference

date/tax point

product code	description	quantity	price	unit	total	discount %	net

terms
Net monthly
Carriage paid
E & OE

goods total	
VAT	
TOTAL	

INVOICE

COMPUWARE.COM LIMITED

Unit 14, Monkwood Estate, Witley Green, MR3 6TH
Tel 01908 765311 Fax 01908 765953 Email compuware@goblin.com
VAT Reg GB 0456 1007 19

invoice to

invoice no 10283

account

your reference

date/tax point

product code	description	quantity	price	unit	total	discount %	net

terms
Net monthly
Carriage paid
E & OE

goods total	
VAT	
TOTAL	

INVOICE

COMPUWARE.COM LIMITED

Unit 14, Monkwood Estate, Witley Green, MR3 6TH
Tel 01908 765311 Fax 01908 765953 Email compuware@goblin.com
VAT Reg GB 0456 1007 19

invoice to

invoice no 10284

account

your reference

date/tax point

product code	description	quantity	price	unit	total	discount %	net

terms
Net monthly
Carriage paid
E & OE

goods total	
VAT	
TOTAL	

REQUESTS FOR CREDIT RECEIVED BY COMPUWARE.COM

To address <compuware@goblin.com>
From: Star Insurance <StarIB@u-net.com>
Subject: Shortages on Delivery
Date: 12.06.04.09.30.34

To Accounts Department

Order Reference 2444

We attach a copy of your quotation dated 1 May, which does not agree with your subsequent invoice 10214 for £935.00 less trade discount + VAT. Please issue a credit note for the difference.

Regards

Jane Salter
Accounts Department (Purchases Ledger)

QUOTATION

COMPUWARE.COM LIMITED

Unit 14, Monkwood Estate, Witley Green, MR3 6TH
Tel 01908 765311 Fax 01908 765953 Email compuware@goblin.com
VAT Reg GB 0456 1007 19

To
Star Insurance Brokers
7 Broad Street
Mereford
MR1 7CF

Date: 01 05 2004

Thank you for your enquiry. We have pleasure in providing the following quotation:

Goods description:

Wizbooks Accounting Software
supply and delivery

£900 less your normal trade discount, plus VAT

signature Mark Allen, Sales Administrator date 1 May 2004

King Designs Limited
45 High Road
Hexworth
HW3 6VB
01804 876293
VAT REG GB 7612 8244 12

RETURNS NOTE

Compuware.com Limited
Unit 14 Monkwood Estate
Witley Green
MR3 6TH

returns note no **1073**
date **08 06 04**

product code	quantity	description
101045	**1**	**Digiviz digital camera @ £695**

REASON FOR RETURN *Faulty goods – please credit in full*

signature *A R King* date *08/06/04*

To address <compuware@goblin.com>
From: D Shaw & Partners <DShawPartners@u-net.com>
Subject: Non delivery of order
Date: 12.06.04.10.34.16

To Accounts Department

Order Reference 2954

On 29 May we ordered (PO ref 2954) 1 x Zap CD writer and a box of 10 CDs. We have received your invoice but not the goods. Please cancel the order and credit in full.

Bertie Shaw
Accounts Department (Purchases Ledger)

DELIVERY NOTE

COMPUWARE.COM LIMITED

Unit 14, Monkwood Estate, Witley Green, MR3 6TH
Tel 01908 765311 Fax 01908 765953 Email compuware@goblin.com
VAT Reg GB 0456 1007 19

D Shaw & Partners
Equity House
The Square
Pithwick PW2 7FG

delivery note no **68873**
delivery method **Puma Parcels**
your order **2954**
date **02 06 04**

product code	quantity	description
102007	1	Zap65 CD writer @ £495
103007	1 box of 10	Zap CD diskpack @ £49.50

Received

signature *B Speers* name (capitals) *B SPEERS* date *06 06 04*

CREDIT NOTE

COMPUWARE.COM LIMITED

Unit 14, Monkwood Estate, Witley Green, MR3 6TH
Tel 01908 765311 Fax 01908 765953 Email compuware@goblin.com
VAT Reg GB 0456 1007 19

to

credit note no **1071**

account

your reference

our invoice

date/tax point

product code	description	quantity	price	unit	total	discount %	net

reason for credit:

goods total	
VAT	
TOTAL	

CREDIT NOTE

COMPUWARE.COM LIMITED

Unit 14, Monkwood Estate, Witley Green, MR3 6TH
Tel 01908 765311 Fax 01908 765953 Email compuware@goblin.com
VAT Reg GB 0456 1007 19

to

credit note no 1072

account

your reference

our invoice

date/tax point

product code	description	quantity	price	unit	total	discount %	net

reason for credit:

goods total	
VAT	
TOTAL	

COMPUWARE.COM LIMITED

Unit 14, Monkwood Estate, Witley Green, MR3 6TH
Tel 01908 765311 Fax 01908 765953 Email compuware@goblin.com
VAT Reg GB 0456 1007 19

CUSTOMER CHEQUES FOR CHECKING

Albion Bank PLC Date *4 June 2004* **90 47 17**

7 The Avenue
Broadfield BR1 2AJ

Pay *Compuware.com Ltd*

Eight thousand five hundred and sixty pounds only £ *8,560.00*

A/c payee only

HARPNEY LIMITED

K C Watt *L Richards*

Director Director

083772 90 47 17 11719881

WESTSIDE BANK PLC Date **78 37 17**

22 Cornbury Street
Shelford SL1 2DC

Pay *Compuware.com Limited*

Three thousand four hundred and fifty pounds only £ *3,450.00*

A/c payee only

KING DESIGNS LIMITED

J King *R Singh*

Director Director

072628 78 37 17 23487611

WESTSIDE BANK PLC Date 7 June 2000 **78 86 34**

22 Market Street
Pithwick PW1 2RD

Pay Compuware.com Limited

Ten thousand four hundred and sixty two pounds 33p £ 10,462.33

A/c payee only

D SHAW & PARTNERS

DShaw Rick Shaw

072628 78 86 34 91030134

Britannia Bank PLC Date *5 June 2004* 33 44 07

89 High Street
Broadfield BR1 8GH

Pay *Compuware.com Limited*

Seven thousand five hundred pounds only A/c payee only £ *7,500.00*

BRINKMAN & CO

987482 33 44 07 24221913

Enigma Bank PLC Date *10 June 2004* 11 63 09

17 High Street
Hereford HR1 2AJ

Pay *Compuware.com Ltd*

Eight thousand eight hundred and thirty five pounds 10p A/c payee only £ *8,835.10*

HELLROSE ASSOCIATES

D Monn *R De Ville*

083772 11 63 09 24294913

Note

The above cheque from Hellrose Associates was accompanied by a remittance advice with the following note attached:

> The attached cheque for £8835.10 is in settlement of your invoice of 31 May for £9,027.91. We have taken settlement discount of £192.81. Please can you now confirm that our account is now paid in full. Many thanks.

The aged debtor summary as at 31 May 2004 shows the following entry for Hellrose Associates:

Customer	Account	Total	0-30 days	30-60 days	60 days and over
Hellrose Associates	3470	12750.70	9027.91	3722.79	nil

Notes for Task 6(a)

COMPUWARE.COM LIMITED

Unit 14, Monkwood Estate, Witley Green, MR3 6TH

Tel 01908 765311 Fax 01908 765953 Email compuware@goblin.com

VAT Reg GB 0456 1007 19

STATEMENT OF ACCOUNT

COMPUWARE.COM LIMITED

Unit 14, Monkwood Estate, Witley Green, MR3 6TH
Tel 01908 765311 Fax 01908 765953 Email compuware@goblin.com
VAT Reg GB 0456 1007 19

TO

account

date

date	details	debit £	credit £	balance £

AMOUNT NOW DUE £

STATEMENT OF ACCOUNT

COMPUWARE.COM LIMITED

Unit 14, Monkwood Estate, Witley Green, MR3 6TH
Tel 01908 765311 Fax 01908 765953 Email compuware@goblin.com
VAT Reg GB 0456 1007 19

TO

account

date

date	details	debit £	credit £	balance £

AMOUNT NOW DUE £

TILL SUMMARY SHEET

Till no 1 Cashier **Jade Mason** Date **4 June 2004**

CASH RECEIVED

Denomination	number	amount (£)
£50 notes	3	
£20 notes	12	
£10 notes	42	
£5 notes	8	
£2 coins	4	
£1 coins	24	
50p coins	16	
20p coins	12	
10p coins	23	
5p coins	7	
2p coins	14	
1p coins	17	

TOTAL CASH

CHEQUES RECEIVED

Name	amount (£)
J Smith	50.00
R Patel	87.75
K Simmons	45.95
K Burton	45.95

TOTAL CHEQUES	
TOTAL DEBIT CARD RECEIPTS	3,678.90
TOTAL CREDIT CARD RECEIPTS	7,570.50
TOTAL TILL RECEIPTS	

TILL SUMMARY SHEET

Till no **2** Cashier **Rashid Singh** Date **4 June 2004**

CASH RECEIVED

Denomination	number	amount (£)
£50 notes	4	
£20 notes	11	
£10 notes	31	
£5 notes	4	
£2 coins	6	
£1 coins	31	
50p coins	12	
20p coins	11	
10p coins	36	
5p coins	9	
2p coins	20	
1p coins	8	
TOTAL CASH		

CHEQUES RECEIVED

Name	amount (£)
R Hazel	49.50
J Nutt	99.60
W Tell	78.50
R Cox	120.50
K Permain	99.95

TOTAL CHEQUES	
TOTAL DEBIT CARD RECEIPTS	1,245.90
TOTAL CREDIT CARD RECEIPTS	5,470.85
TOTAL TILL RECEIPTS	

BANK SUMMARY SHEET

Date 4 June 2004

CASH RECEIVED

Denomination	amount (£)
£50 notes	
£20 notes	
£10 notes	
£5 notes	
£2 coins	
£1 coins	
50p coins	
20p coins	
10p coins	
5p coins	
2p coins	
1p coins	

TOTAL CASH

CHEQUES RECEIVED

	amount (£)
Till 1	
Till 2	

TOTAL CHEQUES

TOTAL BANKED

Date banked ____________

Summary prepared by ______________________________

Date ____________

Cashier's stamp and initials

bank giro credit

Code no	46 76 88
Bank	Western Bank PLC
Branch	Witley Green

Credit: Compuware.com Limited

Account No.: 12034765

Number of cheques

Paid in by ____________

Do not write below this line

	£	p
£50 notes		
£20 notes		
£10 notes		
£5 notes		
£2/£1		
50p		
20p		
10p,5p		
Bronze		
Total Cash		
Cheques etc		
£		

Details of cheques etc	Amount	
TOTAL CARRIED OVER £		

SALES DAY BOOK

Date	Details	Invoice No	Total £ p	VAT £ p	Net £ p

SALES RETURNS DAY BOOK

Date	Details	Credit Note No	Total £ p	VAT £ p	Net £ p

MAIN (GENERAL) LEDGER

Sales

Date 2004	Details	Amount £ p	Date 2004	Details	Amount £ p
			1 Jun	Balance b/d	224,736.50

Sales returns

Date 2004	Details	Amount £ p	Date 2004	Details	Amount £ p
1 Jun	Balance b/d	7,493.25			

Sales Ledger Control

Date 2004	Details	Amount £ p	Date 2004	Details	Amount £ p
1 Jun	Balance b/d	115,751.50			

Value Added Tax

Date 2004	Details	Amount £ p	Date 2004	Details	Amount £ p
			1 Jun	Balance b/d	8,321.35

Discount Allowed

Date 2004	Details	Amount £ p	Date 2004	Details	Amount £ p

Cash Book: Receipts

Date 2004	Details	Discount allowed £ p	Cash £ p	Bank £ p
1 Jun	Balances b/d		115.00	11,207.25

SUBSIDIARY (SALES) LEDGER

Harpney Limited (account no 3412)

Date	Details	Amount	Date	Details	Amount
2004		£ p	2004		£ p
1 Jun	Balance b/d	8,560.00			

Brinkman Limited (account no 3520)

Date	Details	Amount	Date	Details	Amount
2004		£ p	2004		£ p
1 Jun	Balance b/d	18,960.50			

King Designs Limited (account no 3340)

Date 2004	Details	Amount £ p	Date 2004	Details	Amount £ p
1 Jun	Balance b/d	3,450.00			

D Shaw & Partners (account no 3401)

Date 2004	Details	Amount £ p	Date 2004	Details	Amount £ p
1 Jun	Balance b/d	25,500.60			

Star Insurance Brokers (account no 3521)

Date 2004	Details	Amount £ p	Date 2004	Details	Amount £ p
1 Jun	Balance b/d	1,960.80			

Hellrose Associates (account no 3470)

Date 2004	Details	Amount £ p	Date 2004	Details	Amount £ p
1 Jun	Balance b/d	12,750.70			

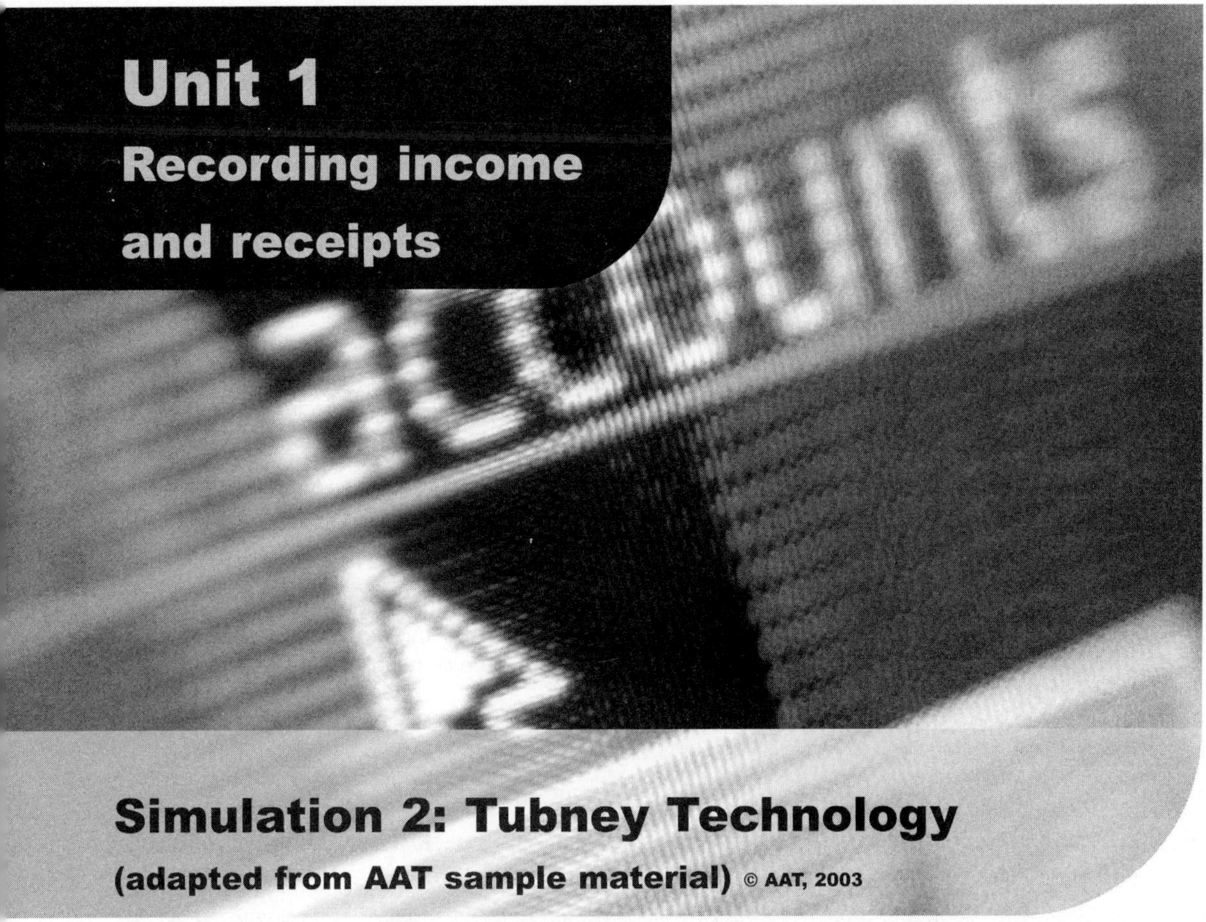

Unit 1
Recording income and receipts

Simulation 2: Tubney Technology
(adapted from AAT sample material) © AAT, 2003

NVQ Element coverage

1.1 process documents relating to goods and services supplied

1.2 process receipts

Scenario and contents

This Simulation is based on Tubney Technology Limited, a company which manufactures parts used in the production of computers and mobile phones. The company sells on credit to its customers and operates an accounting system which is partially computerised.

The tasks in the Simulation include:

- preparation and checking of customer invoices from orders received
- preparation and checking of credit notes in reply to requests for credit
- recording credit transactions in the appropriate accounting records
- preparing statements of account to be sent to customers
- checking cash receipts, cheques and automated receipts and entering them in the accounting records
- preparing paying-in documents
- using an Aged Debtors Analysis to monitor customer accounts

Suggested time allocation:three hours plus fifteen minutes reading time

SIMULATION 2
TUBNEY TECHNOLOGY LTD

SITUATION

Tubney Technology Limited is based at a business park in Oxford. It is a small company with a factory where it manufactures standard parts used in the production of computers and mobile phones. It also makes some special parts to the customer's specification.

You are Lynsey Jones, Accounts Assistant. You report directly to Samir Aleffi, who is the Accounts Manager of Tubney Technology Ltd.

All sales are made on credit to customers, which are computer and mobile phone manufacturers. Tubney Technology Ltd is registered for VAT and all its sales are standard rated at 17.5%.

A settlement discount of 3.5% for payment within 14 days is offered to all customers. Standard payment terms are otherwise 30 days. Established customers also receive trade discount.

ACCOUNTING SYSTEM

Tubney Technology Ltd operates a partially computerised sales and accounting system.

- Invoices and credit notes are prepared manually and details are input to a computer, which produces a Discount Analysis.
- The Sales Day Book and Sales Returns Day Book are prepared manually. The relevant totals are entered by hand into the manual main ledger containing a debtors control account, and into the manual subsidiary (sales) ledger, which is not part of the double entry system.
- Receipts are entered first into the manual cash book, which is part of the main ledger, and this is posted manually to the other main ledger accounts and the subsidiary (sales) ledger. Details of receipts are also entered into the computer, which produces the Aged Debtors Analysis.

Today's date is Thursday 18 September 2003.

TASKS

PART 1: PROCESS DOCUMENTS RELATING TO GOODS AND SERVICES SUPPLIED

Recommended time allocation 90 minutes

Invoice Preparation

All sales to customers are made against purchase orders received from the customer, or sales orders prepared by the Sales Manager, Mark Alberts. For sales of special parts there is also a quotation setting out the work to be done and the rates to be charged. Delivery notes accompany all deliveries to the customer. If the order and the delivery note do not agree in any respect, the sale is not invoiced but is referred back to Mark Alberts. The prices charged are calculated with reference to either the quotation or the price list on page 173. Trade discount details are taken from the Subsidiary (Sales) Ledger Account List, which is also on page 173.

1 Refer to the documents on pages 174-178.

Check each order against the relevant delivery note. Make a note of any discrepancy on page 186.

Prepare invoices for the sales that you have agreed. Use the invoice forms on pages 187-190. You do not need to fill in the customer's address. VAT, trade discount and settlement discount should be rounded down to the nearest penny.

Credit Note Preparation

Credit notes for parts returned are raised against return notes. The return notes are completed and signed by Ian Smith, the Factory Manager, to indicate that he has approved the return.

2 Refer to the returns notes on page 179.

Prepare credit notes using the credit note forms on pages 191-192. You do not need to fill in the customer's address.

3 Before invoices and credit notes are despatched to customers or recorded, they must be authorised.

On page 193, make a note of who should authorise the invoices and credit notes for despatch: Mark Alberts (Sales Manager), Samir Aleffi (Accounts Manager) or Ian Smith (Factory Manager).

Assume that you have obtained authorisation as required.

Make appropriate entries in the Sales Day Book and the Sales Returns Day Book on pages 193-194.

Calculate the total settlement discount that the computer's Discount Analysis will show is available to customers on the day's invoice. Make a note on page 193.

4 Total the entries in the Sales Day Book and Sales Returns Day Book (pages 193 and 194)

Insert the appropriate main ledger and subsidiary (sales) ledger codes in the Day Books.

Make the necessary entries in the main ledger and subsidiary (sales) ledger accounts on pages 195-199. (For some ledger accounts there will be no entries at this stage).

Note: There are transactions already shown on some of the ledger accounts. You do NOT need to balance any accounts after you have made your entries.

PART 2: PROCESS RECEIPTS (90 MINUTES)

Banking Receipts

Cash and cheques received from customers are checked against supporting documentation and then entered into the cash book. Some customers make automated payments, which appear on the bank statement. These are entered into the cash book when they have been checked to the weekly bank statement, and the supporting documentation.

Where the receipt does not agree with supporting documentation, the payment is banked and entered into the cash book, but a communication is sent to the customer outlining the effect of the transaction on the debtor's account. Wrongly completed cheques are returned to the customer with a request for a correctly completed cheque to be issued.

5 Refer to the documents relating to amounts received (pages 181-183), and the subsidiary (sales) ledger accounts (pages 197-199).

Refer to the Discount Analysis printout on page 180 and check the receipt and remittance advices (pages 181-183) to ensure that any settlement discount taken by customers is allowable. You should bear in mind that only a 14 day period is offered and that the month of August has 31 days. Make notes on page 199 of any queries, and the action that needs to be taken.

On page 200, calculate a total for the cash received from Kendrick & Co, and agree this to the receipt that Samir gave to the customer.

Check that the cheques have been correctly completed and agree with supporting documentation. If a cheque cannot be paid into the bank today, or does not agree with supporting documentation, make notes on page 199 as to the reason, and the action that needs to be taken.

Agree the automated receipt on the bank statement on page 184 to the supporting documentation.

6 Write up the cash book (receipts side) on page 201 for the cash and cheques that will be paid into the bank, and subtotal the amount to be paid in.

Write up the cash book (receipts side) for the automated payment received.

Note: You do NOT need to calculate any totals in the cash book (receipts side) at this stage.

7 Prepare the paying-in slip on page 202 for the cash and cheques that need to be paid into the bank today. Make sure that the total on the paying-in slip agrees with paying-in total in the cash book total (receipts side) that you calculated in Task 6.

8 Calculate the totals for the cash book (receipts side).

Enter appropriate main ledger and subsidiary (sales) ledger codes into the cash book (receipts side) in preparation for posting.

Post the cash book (receipts side) into the relevant main ledger and subsidiary (sales) ledger accounts.

9 For the two customers for whom statements are provided on page 203:

- calculate a balance on the appropriate subsidiary (sales) ledger account
- complete the statements as at today's date.

Chasing Payments and Computer Accounting Systems

The company policy for debtors who have debts which are more than 60 days old is to put the whole account on 'stop'. This means that no more sales are made until settlement has been received as agreed.

10 Refer to the extract from the Aged Debtor Analysis on page 184, and to the letter from Kendrick & Co to Mark Alberts on page 185. Samir has made some notes on both documents.

Draft a letter to Slomax & Partners from Samir Aleffi, in accordance with Samir's notes on the Aged Debtor Analysis. Use the letterhead on page 204. Note that the contact name and address for the customer have been completed for you.

Draft a memo to Mark Alberts concerning the letter from Kendrick & Co and Samir's notes on it. Use the memo on page 205.

11 Samir is not completely happy with the fact that Tubney Technology uses a mix of manual and computer accounting systems. He asks you to look into the advantages and disadvantages of using a fully computerised accounting system and suggests that you email him with a summary of your findings in bullet point format (see email on page 206).

DATA

MAIN LEDGER ACCOUNT CODES (EXTRACT)	
Ledger code	**Account name**
1000	Cash
2000	Debtors Control
3000	Discount Allowed
4000	Sales
5000	Sales Returns
6000	VAT

SUBSIDIARY (SALES) LEDGER ACCOUNT CODES (EXTRACT)		
Ledger code	**Account name**	**Trade discount**
100	Ardington plc	0
200	Dreadnought PC Ltd	5%
300	Kendrick & Co	0
400	Lineman plc	0
500	PrimeTime Mobiles	5%
600	Rondar plc	0
700	Slomax & Partners	0

TUBNEY TECHNOLOGY LTD: PRICE LIST	
Part reference	**£ per unit**
AD897	0.35
DF014	3.60
GW208	12.80
MM936	0.50
PA220	5.55
RL188	9.75

QUOTATION

From: Tubney Technology Ltd, Oxford Business Park, Oxford OX2 8VN

To: Dreadnought PC Ltd
Saddleworth Lane
Halifax LS6 8WL

Date: 8 September 2003

Further to your enquiry, we have pleasure in providing this firm quotation to carry out the necessary work as per your specification.

DESCRIPTION

Manufacture and testing of 500 HighDensity 10cm SIM cards as per your specification of 1 September 2003.

Including packing and delivery £1,950 plus VAT

Signed: *M Alberts* Date: 8 September 2003

PURCHASE ORDER

Ardington plc
90/94 Grove Road
Wantage OX16 9AS

To: Tubney Technology Ltd, Oxford Business Park, Oxford OX2 8VN

Date: 15 September 2003

Please supply us with 2,000 AD897 and 1,000 MM936 parts as soon as possible.

Yours faithfully

C Timms

Ardington plc

DELIVERY NOTE

From: Tubney Technology Ltd, Oxford Business Park, Oxford, OX2 8VN

Delivered to: Ardington plc
90/94 Grove Road
Wantage OX16 9AS

Date: 16 September 2003

ITEM	QUANTITY
MM936	1,000
AD897	2,000

Received by: *C Timms* Date: *16 September 2003*

PURCHASE ORDER

Dreadnought PC Ltd
Saddleworth Lane
Halifax LS6 8WL

To: Tubney Technology Ltd, Oxford Business Park, Oxford OX2 8VN

Date: 10 September 2003

Please supply 500 special parts in accordance with your quotation of 8 September, which we accept.

Yours faithfully

S Parsons

Dreadnought PC Ltd

DELIVERY NOTE

From: Tubney Technology Ltd, Oxford Business Park, Oxford OX2 8VN

Delivered to: Dreadnought PC Ltd
Saddleworth Lane
Halifax LS6 8WL

Date: 16 September 2003

ITEM	QUANTITY
HighDensity 10cm SIM Cards as per quotation	500

Received by: *S Parsons* Date: *16 September 2003*

PURCHASE ORDER

Kendrick & Co
110-120 Banbury Road
Bicester OX6 9QW

To: Tubney Technology Ltd
Oxford Business Park
Oxford OX2 8VN

Date: 15 September 2003

Please supply 100 PA220 parts as soon as possible.

Yours faithfully

O Kendrick

Kendrick & Co

DELIVERY NOTE

From: Tubney Technology Ltd, Oxford Business Park, Oxford OX2 8VN

Delivered to: Kendrick & Co
110-120 Banbury Road
Bicester OX6 9QW

Date: 17 September 2003

ITEM	QUANTITY
RL188	1,000

Received by: *O Kendrick* Date: 17 September 2003

SALES ORDER

Tubney Technology Ltd, Oxford Business Park, Oxford OX2 8VN

Customer: Lineman plc

Deliver to: Hamilton House
Oxford Science Park
Oxford OX3 3PR

Date: 15 September 2003

ITEM	QUANTITY
AD897	3,000
DF014	200
GW208	150

Order taken by: *M Alberts* Date: *15 September 2003*

DELIVERY NOTE

From: Tubney Technology Ltd, Oxford Business Park, Oxford OX2 8VN

Delivered to: Lineman plc
Hamilton House
Oxford Science Park
Oxford OX3 3PR

Date: 17 September 2003

ITEM	QUANTITY
GW208	150
DF014	200
AD897	3,000

Received by: P Patel Date: 17 September 2003

SALES ORDER

Tubney Technology Ltd, Oxford Business Park, Oxford OX2 8VN

Customer: PrimeTime Mobiles

Deliver to: Penny Hinton Road
Morpath
Cambridge CB13 8DF

Date: 16 September 2003

ITEM	QUANTITY
PA220	250
MM936	3,000

Order taken by: *M Alberts* Date: *16 September 2003*

DELIVERY NOTE

From: Tubney Technology Ltd, Oxford Business Park, Oxford OX2 8VN

Delivered to: PrimeTime Mobiles
Penny Hinton Road
Morpath
Cambridge CB13 8DF

Date: 17 September 2003

ITEM	QUANTITY
PA220	250
MM936	3,000

Received by: *A Colley* Date: *17 September 2003*

RETURNS NOTE

Tubney Technology Ltd, Oxford Business Park, Oxford OX2 8VN

Customer: Kendrick & Co

Date: 12 September 2003

ITEM RETURNED	QUANTITY
GW208 see invoice 8900 8 Sept 2003	20

Reason for return Faulty parts

Received by: *Ian Smith* Date: *12 September 2003*

RETURNS NOTE

Tubney Technology Ltd, Oxford Business Park, Oxford OX2 8VN

Customer: Rondar plc

Date: 15 September 2003

ITEM RETURNED	QUANTITY
PA220 see invoice 8905 10 Sept 03	15

Reason for return Faulty parts

Received by: *Ian Smith* Date: *15 September 2003*

DISCOUNT ANALYSIS (EXTRACT)

Invoice number	Date 2003	Customer account	SDB folio	Invoice subtotal £	VAT £	Invoice total £	Settlement discount £
8750	19 Sept	Dreadnought PC Ltd	200	8,550.00	1,443.88	9,993.88	299.25
8765	20 Aug	PrimeTime Mobiles	500	4,264.05	616.05	4,264.05	127.68
8790	22 Aug	Ardington plc	100	438.75	74.09	512.84	15.35
8890	5 Sept	Kendrick & Co	300	360.00	60.79	420.79	12.60
8910	8 Sept	Lineman plc	400	487.50	82.32	569.82	17.06

RECEIPT no: 51

18 September 2003

To: Barry Kendrick, Kendrick & Co

Receipt for cash received

Received with thanks £408.19 in full settlement of Invoice 8890 (discount taken: £12.60).

S Aleffi

Accounts Manager

Tubney Technology Ltd

REMITTANCE ADVICE

Ardington plc

90/94 Grove Road, Wantage OX16 9AS

To: Tubney Technology Ltd, Oxford Business Park, Oxford OX2 8VN

Date	Transaction reference	Amount (£)
28 Aug 03	Invoice 8790	512.84
17 Sept 03	Cheque attached	-512.84

Minster Bank PLC
16 Broad Street
Oxford OX2 7DF

date 17 Sept 2003

25-45-78

Pay Tubney Technology Limited

Account payee only

Five hundred and twelve pounds 84p only

£ 512.84

ARDINGTON PLC

C Timms

455847 254578 03216875

MITTANCE ADVICE

rimeTime Mobiles

Penny Hinton Road, Morpath, Cambridge CB13 8DF

To: Tubney Technology Ltd, Oxford Business Park, Oxford OX2 8VN

Date	Transaction reference	Amount (£)
21 Aug 03	Invoice 8765	4,264.05
17 Sept 03	Cheque attached	- 4,264.05

Anglia Bank PLC
11 Castle Street
Cambridge CB2 7DF

date 17 Sept 2003

35-45-91

Pay Tubney Technology Limited

Account payee only

only

Four thousand two hundred and sixty four pounds 05p

£ 4,264.05

PrimeTime Mobiles

464647 354591 77575461

REMITTANCE ADVICE

Dreadnought PC Ltd

Saddleworth Lane, Halifax LS6 8WL

To: Tubney Technology Ltd, Oxford Business Park, Oxford OX2 8VN

Date	Transaction reference	Amount (£)
19 Aug 03	Invoice 8750	9,939.88
17 Sept 03	Cheque attached	- 9,939.88

Eboracum Bank PLC
Denby Road
Halifax LS9 7FG

date 17 Sept 2003

50 46 30

Pay Tubney Technology Limited

only

Nine thousand, nine hundred and thirty nine pounds 88p

£ 9,939.88

Account payee only

DREADNOUGHT PC LTD

K Betts

302695 504630 97198715

REMITTANCE ADVICE

LINEMAN PLC

Hamilton House, Oxford Science Park, Oxford OX3 3PR

To: Tubney Technology Ltd, Oxford Business Park, Oxford OX2 8VN

Date	Transaction reference	Amount (£)
8 Sept 03	Invoice 8910	569.82
17 Sept 03	BACS payment	- 552.76
17 Sept 03	Settlement discount taken	- 17.06

Minster Bank plc

High Street, Oxford OX2 7DF

STATEMENT

Account name: Tubney Technology Ltd

Statement no: 109

Account number: 98746510

Sort code: 25-45-78

Details	Date	Payments	Receipts	Balance
	2003			
Balance forward	11 Sept			25,946.46 Cr
CC	11 Sept		9,457.08	
Cheque 4900	11 Sept	15,789.43		
Cheque 4899	11 Sept	6,913.30		12,700.81 Cr
CC	12 Sept		12,879.63	
Cheques 4901	12 Sept	8,673.00		
CC	12 Sept		500.00	17,407.44 Cr
BACS payment – salaries	15 Sept	21,067.90		
CC	15 Sept		7,560.49	3,900.03 Cr
Cheque 4902	16 Sept	681.34		
BACS receipt	17 Sept		552.76	3,771.45 Cr

Key CC: Cash and/or cheques BACS: Bankers Automated Clearing Service

AGED DEBTOR ANALYSIS (EXTRACT)

Customer	Subsidiary (sales) ledger code	Credit limit £	Total £	Not yet due 0-30 days £	30–60 days £	60+ days £
Slomax & Partners	700	2,000.00	3,972.09	0.00	1,893.44	2,078.65

NOTE: In error we allowed them to exceed their credit limit, then we received a cheque dated 16 September 2002 for £2,078.65, plus an order for goods worth £1,280.00. Draft a letter for my signature – point out why we could not bank this cheque (which we will return with the letter, asking for a corrected one), and confirm our company policy on the state of their account.

Kendrick & Co

110-120 Banbury Road

Bicester OX6 9QW

Phone: 01869 654641 Fax: 01869 567684

Mr M Alberts
Sales Manager
Tubney Technology Ltd
Oxford Business Park
Oxford OX2 8VN

16 September 2003

Dear Mark

As you know, I often pay your invoices in cash, so that we can take advantage of the settlement discount you offer. I have recently acquired a corporate credit card. If you are agreeable, I propose to pay our bills in future by this method. I shall pop in on Friday to settle our account as it stands in full with the card.

Yours sincerely

O Kendrick

Ollie Kendrick

Partner

Lynsey

Mark and his sales team are able to take credit card payments using vouchers, but our floor limit is only £100. What is the state of Kendrick & Co's account currently? Will they be able to settle it in full on Friday? Please drop a memo to Mark about this, and let me have a copy.

Samir

ANSWER PAGES

Task 1

Note on sale not invoiced

Action to be taken

Note on sale not invoiced

Action to be taken

INVOICE

Tubney Technology Limited

Oxford Business Park
Oxford OX2 8VN

Tel 01865 444555
Fax 01865 444666
VAT Reg 305 034 97 63

customer:

invoice no. 8950

date

Subsidiary (sales) ledger code:

quantity	**description/code**	**Price (£)**	**Total (£)**
		Goods total	
		Less trade discount %	
		VAT at 17.5%	
		Invoice total	

Settlement discount:
3.5% for payment within 14 days (to be deducted when computing VAT)

INVOICE

Tubney Technology Limited

Oxford Business Park
Oxford OX2 8VN

Tel 01865 444555
Fax 01865 444666
VAT Reg 305 034 97 63

customer:	**invoice no.** 8951
	date
	Subsidiary (sales) ledger code:

quantity	description/code	Price (£)	Total (£)

Goods total	
Less trade discount %	
VAT at 17.5%	
Invoice total	

Settlement discount:
3.5% for payment within 14 days (to be deducted when computing VAT)

INVOICE

Tubney Technology Limited

Oxford Business Park
Oxford OX2 8VN

Tel 01865 444555
Fax 01865 444666
VAT Reg 305 034 97 63

customer:	**invoice no.** 8952
	date
	Subsidiary (sales) ledger code:

quantity	description/code	Price (£)	Total (£)

Goods total	
Less trade discount %	
VAT at 17.5%	
Invoice total	

Settlement discount:
3.5% for payment within 14 days (to be deducted when computing VAT)

INVOICE

Tubney Technology Limited

Oxford Business Park
Oxford OX2 8VN

Tel 01865 444555
Fax 01865 444666
VAT Reg 305 034 97 63

customer:

invoice no. 8953

date

Subsidiary (sales) ledger code:

quantity	**description/code**	**Price (£)**	**Total (£)**

Goods total	
Less trade discount %	
VAT at 17.5%	
Invoice total	

Settlement discount:
3.5% for payment within 14 days (to be deducted when computing VAT)

CREDIT NOTE

Tubney Technology Limited

Oxford Business Park
Oxford OX2 8VN

Tel 01865 444555
Fax 01865 444666
VAT Reg 305 034 97 63

customer:

credit note no. 650

date

Subsidiary (sales) ledger code:

quantity	description/code	Price (£)	Total (£)

Less trade discount %	
VAT at 17.5%	
credit note total	

CREDIT NOTE

Tubney Technology Limited

Oxford Business Park
Oxford OX2 8VN

Tel 01865 444555
Fax 01865 444666
VAT Reg 305 034 97 63

customer:

credit note no. 651

date

Subsidiary (sales) ledger code:

quantity	description/code	Price (£)	Total (£)

Less trade discount %	
VAT at 17.5%	
credit note total	

Invoices and credit notes should be authorised before despatch by: ____________________

Day's total settlement discount on invoices (to be agreed to Discount Analysis): ____________________

SALES DAY BOOK Folio: SDB 38

Date 2003	Customer	Sales ledger code DR	Invoice number	Total £	VAT £	Net £
Total						
Main ledger codes						

SALES RETURNS DAY BOOK					Folio: SRDB 9	
Date 2003	Customer	Sales ledger code CR	Credit note number	Total £	VAT £	Net £
Total						
Main ledger codes						

MAIN LEDGER

2000 SALES LEDGER CONTROL ACCOUNT

Date 2003	Details	Folio	Amount £	Date 2003	Details	Folio	Amount £

3000 DISCOUNT ALLOWED

Date 2003	Details	Folio	Amount £	Date 2003	Details	Folio	Amount £

4000 SALES

Date 2003	Details	Folio	Amount £	Date 2003	Details	Folio	Amount £

MAIN LEDGER

5000 SALES RETURNS

Date 2003	Details	Folio	Amount £	Date 2003	Details	Folio	Amount £

6000 VAT

Date 2003	Details	Folio	Amount £	Date 2003	Details	Folio	Amount £

SUBSIDIARY (SALES) LEDGER

100 ARDINGTON PLC

Date 2003	Details	Folio	Amount £	Date 2003	Details	Folio	Amount £
22 Aug	Inv 8790	SDB 34	512.84				

200 DREADNOUGHT PC LTD

Date 2003	Details	Folio	Amount £	Date 2003	Details	Folio	Amount £
19 Aug	Inv 8750	SDB 34	9,993.88				

300 KENDRICK & CO

Date 2003	Details	Folio	Amount £	Date 2003	Details	Folio	Amount £
5 Sep	Inv 8890	SDB 36	420.79				
8 Sep	Inv 8900	SDB 37	1,496.16				

SUBSIDIARY (SALES) LEDGER

400 LINEMAN PLC

Date 2003	Details	Folio	Amount £	Date 2003	Details	Folio	Amount £
8 Sep	Inv 8910	SDB 37	569.82				

500 PRIMETIME MOBILES

Date 2003	Details	Folio	Amount £	Date 2003	Details	Folio	Amount £
20 Aug	Inv 8765	SDB 34	4,264.05				

600 RONDAR PLC

Date 2003	Details	Folio	Amount £	Date 2003	Details	Folio	Amount £
13 May	Inv 6535	SDB 7	169.86				
2 Jun	Inv 6590	SDB 10	210.87				

SUBSIDIARY (SALES) LEDGER

700 SLOMAX & PARTNERS

Date 2003	Details	Folio	Amount £	Date 2003	Details	Folio	Amount £
18 Sep	Balance		3,972.09				

Task 5

Notes

Contents of envelope handed in by Mark Albert with Kendrick & Co receipt

		£
£50	4	
£20	8	
£10	4	
£5	1	
£2	0	
£1	2	
50p	1	
20p	2	
10p	1	
5p	3	
2p	1	
1p	2	

MAIN LEDGER: 1000 CASH BOOK CB38

RECEIPTS

Date	Details	Ref	Receipt £	Discount allowed £	Customer account £	Sales ledger code
Main ledger codes						

date ____________

bank giro credit

please list cheques overleaf

Cashier's stamp

Minster Bank Plc
High Street, Oxford, OX2 7DF

Account
Tubney Technology Limited

Paid in by

Notes	£50	
	£20	
	£10	
	£5	
Coins	£2	
	£1	
	50p	
	20p,10p,5p	
	2p,1p	
Total Cash		
Cheques		
£		

number of cheques

sort code: 25-45-78

account number: 98746510

000123 25 45 78 98746510

cheques	amount	
Total cheques carried over		

STATEMENT OF ACCOUNT

Tubney Technology Limited

Oxford Business Park, Oxford OX2 8VN, Tel 01865 444555, Fax 01865 444666

Customer Dreadnought PC Limited

Date

Subsidiary (sales) ledger code

Date	Transaction	Debit £	Credit £	Balance £

Balance outstanding

Our terms are strictly 30 days, with 3.5% cash settlement discount available for payment within 14 days.

STATEMENT OF ACCOUNT

Tubney Technology Limited

Oxford Business Park, Oxford OX2 8VN, Tel 01865 444555, Fax 01865 444666

Customer Kendrick & Co

Date

Subsidiary (sales) ledger code

Date	Transaction	Debit £	Credit £	Balance £

Balance outstanding

Our terms are strictly 30 days, with 3.5% cash settlement discount available for payment within 14 days.

Tubney Technology Limited

Oxford Business Park, Oxford OX2 8VN
Tel: 01865 444555 Fax: 01865 444666

Ms U Ogangwe
Slomax & Partners
Success House
200 Old Kent Road
London SE2 9CV

MEMO

To:

From:

cc:

Subject:

Date:

EMAIL

from	lynsey.jones@tubneytech.co.uk
to	samir.aleffi@tubneytech.co.uk
cc	
subject	Computerisation
date	18 September 2003

message

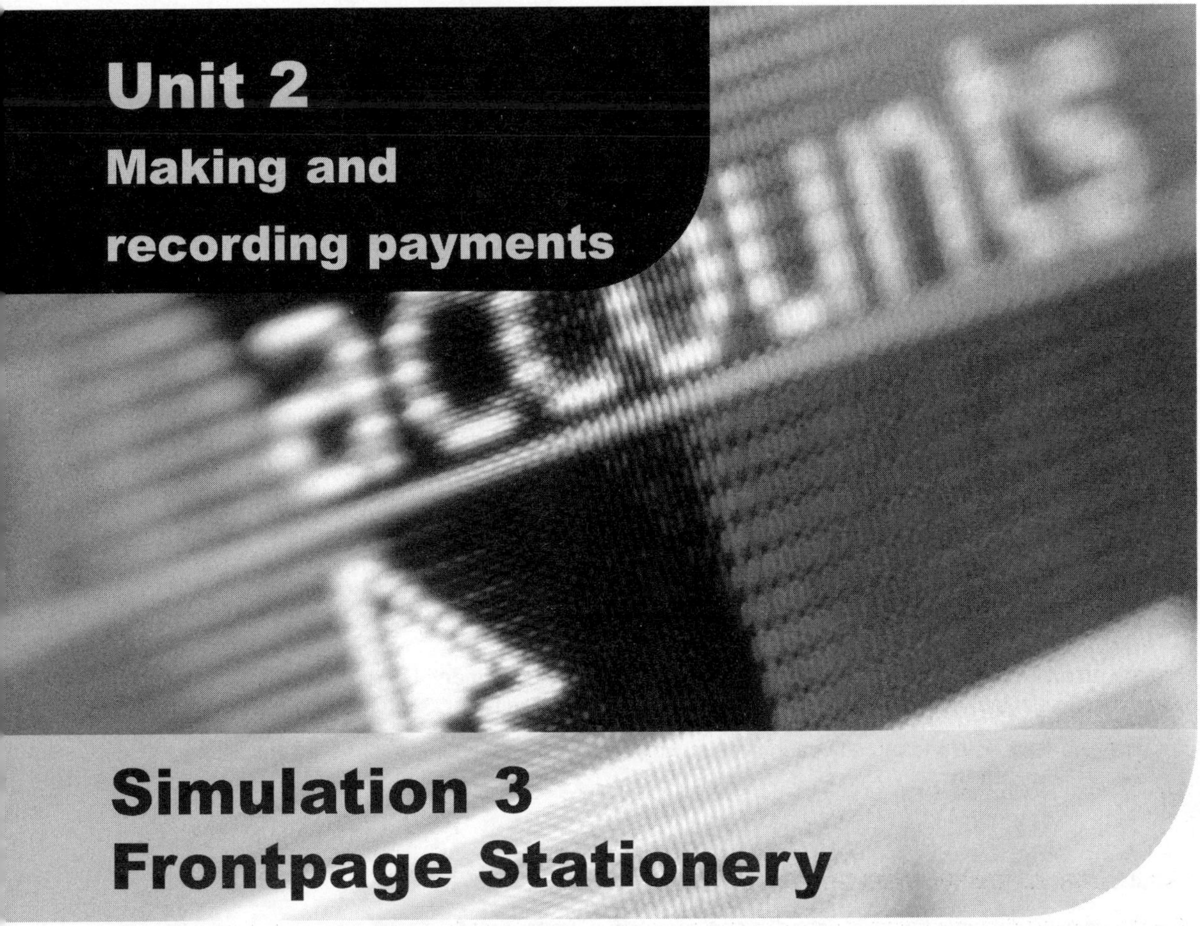

Unit 2
Making and recording payments

Simulation 3
Frontpage Stationery

NVQ Element coverage

2.1 process documents relating to goods and services received

2.2 process payments

Scenario and contents

This Simulation is based on Frontpage Stationery, a sole trader stationery wholesale business run by Jessie Page. The business, which has six employees on the payroll, buys in and supplies stationery to a wide range of businesses. The tasks in the Simulation include:

- checking, coding and approval of suppliers' invoices
- checking, coding and approval of suppliers' credit notes
- making payment by cheque and remittance advice on receipt of suppliers' statements
- paying employees on the payroll and making the PAYE payment to the Inland Revenue
- keeping accounting records up-to-date
- making petty cash payments

Suggested time allocation: three hours plus fifteen minutes reading time

SIMULATION 3
FRONTPAGE STATIONERY

SITUATION

You work as book-keeper for Jessie Page who runs a sole trader wholesale stationery business – Frontpage Stationery – in Knightwick. The business operates from Unit 2 Hillside Trading Estate, Knightwick, MR6 7LP. She employs six staff. Jessie sells by mail order and also from a showroom in the Unit. Her customers are mainly businesses, but she also supplies stationery to schools and colleges. She runs a stationery stall at the local College each September.

Your work involves writing up the accounting records and running the payroll. You have to check suppliers' invoices, despatch notes, credit notes, and statements to ensure that you pay for what you have received, and on the right terms.

You are responsible for running the weekly payroll and for making the monthly PAYE payment to the Inland Revenue. Employees are paid through the Albion Bank 'Auto Credit' BACS payment system.

You are also responsible for a petty cash system which is run on a day-to-day basis by Jessie.

Jessie Page is registered for VAT.

GOODS RECEIVED FROM SUPPLIERS ON CREDIT

Goods received documentation is signed in by the goods-in manager, M Gillibert, who also checks the unit prices against the purchase orders. You then have to check suppliers' terms and conditions and the calculations on suppliers' invoices before passing them for payment (which is normally made when the statement is received).

You also check suppliers' credit notes when they are received to make sure that the correct discount and VAT has been applied.

Any discrepancies on invoices or credit notes which you cannot resolve yourself are referred to Jessie. When discrepancies are sorted out, the invoices or credit notes are passed forward for processing, otherwise they are queried with the supplier by telephone, email or letter.

PETTY CASH

The petty cash is controlled in the normal day-to-day running of the business by Jessie Page. Your job is to check the vouchers and receipts and to write up and balance the petty cash book on a regular basis.

PAYROLL

Jessie Page has six employees on the payroll which is run on a weekly basis. The payroll is operated on a manual basis. Employees are paid through the Albion Bank 'Auto Credit' BACS payment system – you have to complete a bank schedule with the employee payment details each week. The total of the net pay is automatically deducted from the bank account when the sheet is received by the bank. Details of income tax and net National Insurance Contributions to the Inland Revenue are entered weekly on a PAYE summary sheet. The monthly totals from this sheet are sent each month on a bank giro payment (P30B) to the Inland Revenue.

ACCOUNTING RECORDS

Frontpage Stationery records purchases invoices in a purchases day book, and credit notes received in a purchases returns day book. A manual system of double-entry book-keeping is used, with a cash book and a main ledger. The main ledger includes a control account for creditors, with supplier accounts contained in a subsidiary (purchases) ledger.

TASKS

PART 1: DEALING WITH CREDIT PURCHASES

1 Refer to the suppliers' invoices and your goods received notes on pages 212 to 217. The goods received notes have already been checked against the purchase orders.

You are required to perform your usual validation checks on the invoices and to set out your results on the form provided on page 218 You should indicate either that the invoice is approved for payment, or that it is not approved. If it is not approved, you should state clearly the reason(s) why, and the follow-up action you would take. You usually raise invoice queries by letter.

Note that invoices and credit notes approved for processing are given an internal consecutive code number which is written on the document. The next number to use for invoices is 6471 and for credit notes it is 345.

Today's date is 25 July 2004.

2 If there are any invoices which you have not approved, you are required to write an appropriate letter to the supplier(s). The letters (pages 219 - 220) should set out the problem and ask for the appropriate action to be taken.

Use your own name and the date 25 July 2004.

3 Refer to the purchases day book on page 240 which has already been written up to 24 July 2004.

You are to enter all the purchases invoices which you have approved in Task 1 into the purchases day book.

Total the purchases day book and record the accounting entries in the main ledger and subsidiary (purchases) ledger accounts on pages 240 to 244.

Note: opening balances are shown on these accounts where appropriate.

4 On 27 July 2004 you receive a credit note from Meara Limited, one of your regular suppliers (page 221). The credit was agreed earlier in the month and so does not apply to invoice 423 (Task 1, page 215). You are to check the credit note for accuracy (and for any trade discount).

If there is any problem you are to send an email. Draft the text on the email on page 221. Draft the email for the attention of the Accounts Department and sign off with your own name.

5 Refer to the purchases returns day book on page 240 which has already been written up to 24 July 2004.

Total the purchases returns day book and record the accounting entries in the main (general) ledger and subsidiary (purchases) ledger accounts on pages 240 to 244.

PART 2: MAKING AND RECORDING PAYMENTSS

6 On 31 July 2004 Jessie passes you four invoices received in June which have been approved and are now due for payment (pages 222 to 223). She also passes you two approved invoices which qualify for settlement (cash) discount (page 224).

You are to complete the remittance advices and cheques in payment of the six invoices (pages 225 to 230). The remittance advices and cheques should be dated 31 July 2004 but the cheques left unsigned – Jessie Page will sign them when she has checked them.

7 On 27 July 2004 you process the payroll for the six employees of Frontpage Stationery. You have completed a payroll analysis sheet (page 231) from the deduction sheets.

You are to complete an Albion Bank 'Auto Credit' BACS payment schedule (page 232) with the employee payment details from the employee database (page 233) ready for signature by Jessie Page.

The total of the net pay is automatically deducted from the bank account when the sheet is received by the bank.

8 Transfer the information from the payroll analysis sheet into the main (general) ledger accounts for wages & salaries, Inland Revenue, pension fund, and wages & salaries control – these accounts are on pages 242 and 243. Date the entries 27 July 2004.

Note: opening balances are shown on these accounts where appropriate.

9 Record in the cash book (page 242) the six payment cheques from Task 6 and the total of the payroll BACS payment schedule from task 7.

10 Total the cash book and make the entries in the main (general) ledger and subsidiary (purchases) ledger accounts on pages 240 to 244.

11 On 3 August 2004 you are to complete the PAYE deduction summary (page 233). The deduction figures for the first two weeks are already there. You extract the figures for the third week from the payroll analysis sheet (page 231). The figures for the fourth week are:

Income tax collected	£225.00
National Insurance Contributions (employee)	£128.00
National Insurance Contributions (employer)	£156.00

12 Complete the P30B and cheque (page 234) with the PAYE amounts from the PAYE deduction summary (page 233). The cheque is to be made payable to the Inland Revenue and should be dated 3 August 2004; it will be signed by Jessie Page. The P30B will be paid in by yourself on 6 August 2004.

13 Jessie Page operates a petty cash system. The imprest amount is £200.

The guide shown at the top of the next page is written on a sheet of paper which is kept in the petty cash drawer in Jessie's office.

FRONTPAGE PETTY CASH

APPROVED EXPENSES THAT CAN BE REIMBURSED
(Maximum amount claimable £50)
Petrol or diesel fuel (this can only be claimed by sales representatives)
Stationery
Window cleaning (to be analysed as office expenses)
Travelling expenses (only for business purposes)
Stamps and postage
Tea, coffee etc (to be analysed as office expenses).

EXPENSES ON WHICH VAT IS PAYABLE (provided the supplier is VAT registered)
Petrol or diesel fuel
Stationery
Window cleaning
Taxi fares

The date is 3 August 2004 and you have been asked to update the petty cash system. Jessie has topped up the cash box on 1 August to restore the balance to the imprest amount of £200. This opening balance of £200 is shown in the petty cash book (page 235).

You have been presented with ten claims on petty cash vouchers. These are shown, along with supporting receipts where available, on pages 236 to 239.

You are required to authorise those claims which you think are valid and which can be reimbursed out of petty cash. You must sign in your own name in the 'authorised' section of the the appropriate petty cash vouchers.

If you are rejecting any claims you should write the reason on the voucher.

14 All the vouchers which you have authorised are to be entered in the Petty Cash Book provided on page 235. You will have to work out the VAT content of any of the payments which involve VAT (the supplier must be registered for VAT if you are doing this).

The analysis columns must be completed as appropriate.

Total the columns, but do not balance the petty cash book, as this will be done at the end of the month.

INVOICE

FURLONG LIMITED

37 Highfield Trading Estate Lampeter LL4 7YG

internal code number:

invoice to

Frontpage Stationery
Unit 2, Hillside Trading Estate
Knightwick
MR6 7LP

invoice no	7724
account	246
your reference	377
date/tax point	20 07 04

product code	description	quantity	price	unit	total	discount 0%	net
844	Calculator SRP22	30	6.10	each	183.00	0.00	183.00
2634	Dictaphone Z11	25	42.00	each	1050.00	0.00	1050.00

goods total	1233.00
VAT	215.77
TOTAL	1448.77

terms
Net 30 days

INVOICE

Sheppard & Suckling

Hanover House, Lilly Square, London SW3 6BZ

internal code number:

invoice to

Frontpage Stationery
Unit 2, Hillside Trading Estate
Knightwick
MR6 7LP

invoice no	2705
account	4226
your reference	390
date/tax point	18 07 04

product code	description	quantity	price	unit	total	discount 5%	net
B34	Laminated UK map	8	8.80	each	70.40	3.52	66.88
R219	A2 Desk planner	12	9.60	each	115.20	5.76	109.44

goods total	176.32
VAT	30.85
TOTAL	207.17

terms
Net 30 days

INVOICE

Drysdale & Co

13 Berkeley Street, London E4 3BZ

internal code number:

invoice to

Frontpage Stationery
Unit 2, Hillside Trading Estate
Knightwick
MR6 7LP

invoice no	2721
account	5291
your reference	385
date/tax point	20 07 04

product code	description	quantity	price	unit	total	discount 2%	net
5R80	White copy paper 80g	30	5.60	box	280.00	5.60	274.40
MEC5	Manila envelopes C5	50	7.30	box	365.00	7.30	357.70

goods total	632.10
VAT	108.95
TOTAL	741.05

terms
1.5% settlement discount 14 day settlement, Net 30 days

INVOICE

Drysdale & Co

13 Berkeley Street, London E4 3BZ

internal code number:

invoice to

Frontpage Stationery
Unit 2, Hillside Trading Estate
Knightwick
MR6 7LP

invoice no	2849
account	5291
your reference	402
date/tax point	23 07 04

product code	description	quantity	price	unit	total	discount 2%	net
T4000	Tabulabels, 4000 box	40	14.25	box	570.00	11.40	558.60
FX98	Calculator FX98	30	4.80	each	144.00	2.88	141.12

goods total	699.72
VAT	120.61
TOTAL	820.33

terms
1.5% settlement discount 14 day settlement, Net 30 days

INVOICE

Soloman Limited

Bevels Drive, Hornsea, N11 5TG

internal code number:

invoice to

Frontpage Stationery
Unit 2, Hillside Trading Estate
Knightwick
MR6 7LP

invoice no **149**

account **435**

your reference **381**

date/tax point **18 07 04**

product code	description	quantity	price	unit	total	discount 0%	net
180	Photocopier FP180	2	485.00	each	970.00	0.00	970.00

goods total	970.00
VAT	169.75
TOTAL	1139.75

terms
Net 30 days

INVOICE

Nogan Limited

316 Pearse Road, Jackleton AD3 4PY

internal code number:

invoice to

Frontpage Stationery
Unit 2, Hillside Trading Estate
Knightwick
MR6 7LP

invoice no **516**

account **3241**

your reference **385**

date/tax point **20 07 04**

product code	description	quantity	price	unit	total	discount 0%	net
244	Flexi desk light	4	23.00	each	92.00	0.00	92.00
234	Floor uplighter	6	18.50	each	111.00	0.00	111.00
441	Bubble jet printer	1	175.00	each	175.00	0.00	175.00

goods total	378.00
VAT	66.15
TOTAL	444.15

terms
Net 30 days

INVOICE

internal code number:

Putney Limited
Unit 17 Bancroft Estate
Droysley MD14 6ZX

invoice to

Frontpage Stationery
Unit 2, Hillside Trading Estate
Knightwick
MR6 7LP

invoice no **3492**
account **4216**
your reference **388**
date/tax point **17 07 04**

product code	description	quantity	price	unit	total	discount 3%	net
67B	Box files	120	2.10	each	252.00	7.56	244.44
442	Portable fan	6	18.00	each	108.00	3.24	104.76

goods total	349.20
VAT	61.11
TOTAL	410.31

terms
Net 30 days

INVOICE

Meara Limited
45 Crystal Dock,
Thimborough BD17 2ER

internal code number:

invoice to

Frontpage Stationery
Unit 2, Hillside Trading Estate
Knightwick
MR6 7LP

invoice no **423**
account **2711**
your reference **392**
date/tax point **20 07 04**

product code	description	quantity	price	unit	total	discount 5%	net
LP34	Laser printer	2	380.00	each	760.00	38.00	722.00

goods total	722.00
VAT	126.35
TOTAL	848.35

terms
Net 30 days

GOODS RECEIVED NOTE no 2143

Date	*23 July 2004*
Supplier	*Drysdale & Co*
Order no.	*364*

quantity	description
30 boxes	*White copy paper 80g*
50 boxes	*Manila envelopes C5*

received in good condition

M Gillibert

GOODS RECEIVED NOTE no 2144

Date	*23 July 2004*
Supplier	*Soloman Ltd*
Order no.	*381*

quantity	description
2	*Photocopier FP180*

received in good condition

M Gillibert

GOODS RECEIVED NOTE no 2145

Date	*23 July 2004*
Supplier	*Nogan Ltd*
Order no.	*385*

quantity	description
4	*Flexi desk light*
6	*Floor uplighter*

received in good condition

M Gillibert

GOODS RECEIVED NOTE no 2146

Date	*23 July 2004*
Supplier	*Furlong Ltd*
Order no.	*377*

quantity	description
30	*Calculator SRP22*
25	*Dictaphone Z11*

received in good condition

M Gillibert

GOODS RECEIVED NOTE no 2147

Date	*23 July 2004*
Supplier	*Putney Ltd*
Order no.	*388*

quantity	description
120	*Box files*
6	*Portable fans*

received in good condition

M Gillibert

GOODS RECEIVED NOTE no 2148

Date	*23 July 2004*
Supplier	*Meara Ltd*
Order no.	*392*

quantity	description
2	*Laser Printer*

received in good condition

M Gillibert

GOODS RECEIVED NOTE no 2149

Date	*23 July 2004*
Supplier	*Sheppard & Suckling*
Order no.	*390*

quantity	description
8	*Laminated UK map*
12	*A2 Desk planner*

received in good condition

M Gillibert

GOODS RECEIVED NOTE no 2150

Date	*23 July 2004*
Supplier	*Drysdale & Co*
Order no.	*402*

quantity	description
40 boxes	*Tabulabels*
30	*Calculator FX98*

received in good condition

M Gillibert

Supplier/invoice	Action

FRONTPAGE STATIONERY

Unit 2 Hillside Trading Estate, Knightwick, MR6 7LP

Tel 01923 230399 Fax 01923 237995 E-mail frontpage@goblin.com

www.frontpage.co.uk

VAT Reg 2342 6171 89

FRONTPAGE STATIONERY

Unit 2 Hillside Trading Estate, Knightwick, MR6 7LP

Tel 01923 230399 Fax 01923 237995 E-mail frontpage@goblin.com

www.frontpage.co.uk

VAT Reg 2342 6171 89

CREDIT NOTE

Meara Limited

45 Crystal Dock,
Thimborough BD17 2ER

internal code number:

invoice to

Frontpage Stationery
Unit 2, Hillside Trading Estate
Knightwick
MR6 7LP

credit note no **423**

account **2711**

your reference **301**

date/tax point **25 07 04**

product code	description	quantity	price	unit	total	discount	net
SC03	**Imax21 colour scanner**	**1**	**400.00**	**each**	**400.00**	**00.00**	**400.00**

goods total	**400.00**
VAT	**70.00**
TOTAL	**470.50**

reason for credit
Cancelled order – credit as agreed.

To address <mearaltd@netserve.com>
From:<frontpage@goblin.com>

Subject:

Date:

INVOICE
FURLONG LIMITED
37 Highfield Trading Estate Lampeter LL4 7YG

internal code number: 6465

invoice to

Frontpage Stationery
Unit 2, Hillside Trading Estate
Knightwick
MR6 7LP

invoice no	7714
account	246
your reference	333
date/tax point	20 06 04

product code	description	quantity	price	unit	total	discount 0%	net
107BK	Box files (black)	10	5.45	each	54.50	0.00	54.50

goods total	54.50
VAT	9.53
TOTAL	64.03

terms
Net 30 days

INVOICE
Sheppard & Suckling
Hanover House, Lilly Square, London SW3 6BZ

internal code number: 6462

invoice to

Frontpage Stationery
Unit 2, Hillside Trading Estate
Knightwick
MR6 7LP

invoice no	2680
account	4226
your reference	301
date/tax point	13 06 04

product code	description	quantity	price	unit	total	discount 5%	net
4531	Photocopy paper white	18	4.90	ream	88.20	4.41	83.79

goods total	83.79
VAT	14.66
TOTAL	98.45

terms
Net 30 days

INVOICE

Soloman Limited

Bevels Drive, Hornsea, N11 5TG

internal code number: 6464

invoice to

Frontpage Stationery
Unit 2, Hillside Trading Estate
Knightwick
MR6 7LP

invoice no	120
account	435
your reference	335
date/tax point	18 06 04

product code	description	quantity	price	unit	total	discount 0%	net
74523	Hermes fax machine	1	285.00	each	285.00	0.00	285.00

goods total	285.00
VAT	49.87
TOTAL	334.87

terms
Net 30 days

INVOICE

internal code number: 6463

Putney Limited

Unit 17 Bancroft Estate
Droysley MD14 6ZX

invoice to

Frontpage Stationery
Unit 2, Hillside Trading Estate
Knightwick
MR6 7LP

invoice no	3411
account	4216
your reference	271
date/tax point	15 06 04

product code	description	quantity	price	unit	total	discount 3%	net
442	Portable fan	2	18.00	each	36.00	1.08	34.92

goods total	34.92
VAT	6.11
TOTAL	41.03

terms
Net 30 days

INVOICE

Drysdale & Co

13 Berkeley Street, London E4 3BZ

internal code number: 6478

invoice to

Frontpage Stationery
Unit 2, Hillside Trading Estate
Knightwick
MR6 7LP

invoice no	2657
account	5291
your reference	364
date/tax point	25 07 04

product code	description	quantity	price	unit	total	discount 2%	net
6546	Operator chair	2	78.00	each	156.00	3.12	152.88

goods total	152.88
VAT	26.35
TOTAL	179.23

terms
1.5% settlement discount 14 day settlement,
Net 30 days

INVOICE

Drysdale & Co

13 Berkeley Street, London E4 3BZ

internal code number: 6477

invoice to

Frontpage Stationery
Unit 2, Hillside Trading Estate
Knightwick
MR6 7LP

invoice no	2684
account	5291
your reference	367
date/tax point	24 07 04

product code	description	quantity	price	unit	total	discount 2%	net
3534	Apex laminator	1	199.50	each	199.50	3,99	195.51

goods total	195.51
VAT	33.70
TOTAL	229.21

terms
1.5% settlement discount 14 day settlement,
Net 30 days

TO

REMITTANCE ADVICE

FROM

Frontpage Stationery
Unit 2, Hillside Trading Estate
Knightwick
MR6 7LP

Account

Date

date	your reference	our reference	payment amount

CHEQUE TOTAL **£**

Albion Bank PLC
7 High Street
Mereford BR1 2AJ

Date

90 43 15

Pay

A/c payee only

£

FRONTPAGE STATIONERY

083800 90 43 15 17256741

TO

REMITTANCE ADVICE

FROM

Frontpage Stationery
Unit 2, Hillside Trading Estate
Knightwick
MR6 7LP

Account

Date

date	your reference	our reference	payment amount

CHEQUE TOTAL **£**

Albion Bank PLC
7 High Street
Mereford BR1 2AJ

Date

90 43 15

Pay

A/c payee only

£

FRONTPAGE STATIONERY

083801 90 43 15 17256741

TO

REMITTANCE ADVICE

FROM

Frontpage Stationery
Unit 2, Hillside Trading Estate
Knightwick
MR6 7LP

Account

Date

date	your reference	our reference	payment amount

CHEQUE TOTAL **£**

Albion Bank PLC
7 High Street
Mereford BR1 2AJ

Date

90 43 15

Pay

A/c payee only

£

FRONTPAGE STATIONERY

083802 90 43 15 17256741

TO

REMITTANCE ADVICE

FROM

Frontpage Stationery
Unit 2, Hillside Trading Estate
Knightwick
MR6 7LP

Account

Date

date	your reference	our reference	payment amount

CHEQUE TOTAL **£**

Albion Bank PLC
7 High Street
Mereford BR1 2AJ

Date

90 43 15

Pay

A/c payee only

£

FRONTPAGE STATIONERY

083803 90 43 15 17256741

TO

REMITTANCE ADVICE

FROM

Frontpage Stationery
Unit 2, Hillside Trading Estate
Knightwick
MR6 7LP

Account

Date

date	your reference	our reference	payment amount

CHEQUE TOTAL **£**

Albion Bank PLC
7 High Street
Mereford BR1 2AJ

Date

90 43 15

Pay

A/c payee only

£

FRONTPAGE STATIONERY

083804 90 43 15 17256741

TO

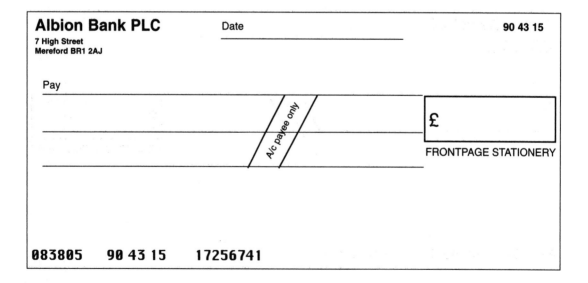

REMITTANCE ADVICE

FROM

Frontpage Stationery
Unit 2, Hillside Trading Estate
Knightwick
MR6 7LP

Account

Date

date	your reference	our reference	payment amount

CHEQUE TOTAL **£**

Albion Bank PLC
7 High Street
Mereford BR1 2AJ

Date

90 43 15

Pay

A/c payee only

£

FRONTPAGE STATIONERY

083805 90 43 15 17256741

FRONTPAGE STATIONERY **payroll analysis sheet** **Week ending** 27 July 2004

employee reference	employee name	Earnings				Deductions				Employer's National Insurance Contributions	Employer's Pension Contributions	Net Pay
		Basic £	Overtime £	Bonus £	Total Gross Pay £	Income Tax £	National Insurance £	Pension Contributions £	Total Deductions £	£	£	£
2345	B Shaw	205.00	25.00	15.00	245.00	35.00	19.50	10.25	64.75	24.50	10.25	180.25
2346	S O'Casey	205.00	10.00	15.00	230.00	32.50	18.00	10.25	60.75	23.05	10.25	169.25
2347	J Osborne	205.00	25.00	15.00	245.00	35.00	19.50	-	54.50	24.50	-	190.50
2348	H Winter	205.00	25.00	15.00	245.00	35.00	19.50	-	54.50	24.50	-	190.50
2349	L Klein	205.00	10.00	15.00	230.00	32.50	18.00	10.25	60.75	23.05	10.25	169.25
2350	T Manning	205.00	25.00	15.00	245.00	35.00	19.50	10.25	64.75	24.50	10.25	180.25
TOTALS		1230.00	120.00	90.00	1440.00	205.00	114.00	41.00	360.00	144.10	41.00	1080.00

Albion Bank PLC
Auto Credit System

Bank branch...Mereford...

Originator name.Frontpage Stationery.........................reference...356345..................

Date...27-07-04..............

Bank sort code	*Account no*	*Name*	*Payee no*	*Amount*

PAYMENT TOTAL

Please make the above payments to reach the payees on ....31 07 04........................(date)

Please debit account no...............................with the sum of £.......................................

authorised signature..

EMPLOYEE DATABASE

Employee	bank sort code	account number	payee number
B Shaw	45-45-62	10386394	1246
S O'Casey	56-67-23	22347342	1250
J Osborne	40-47-07	42472411	1267
H Winter	76-87-44	56944491	1271
L Klein	33-00-77	23442413	1272
T Manning	59-99-01	46244703	1273

PAYE DEDUCTION SUMMARY

week ending	income tax £	NICs (employee) £	NICs (employer) £
13 July 2004	*195.00*	*95.00*	*115.00*
20 July 2004	*201.00*	*105.00*	*135.00*
27 July 2004			
3 August 2004			
TOTALS	**income tax**		
	NICs (employee)		
	NICs (employer)		
	TOTAL PAYE TO P30B		

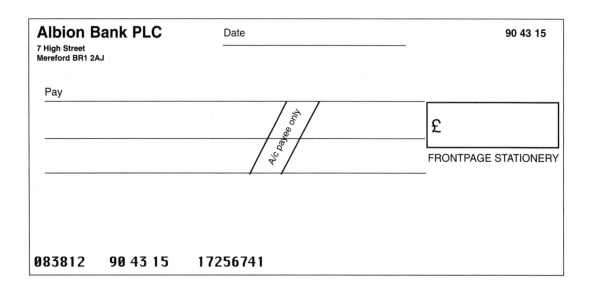

Albion Bank PLC
7 High Street
Mereford BR1 2AJ

Date ______________________ 90 43 15

Pay ______________________________________ A/c payee only

£

FRONTPAGE STATIONERY

083812 90 43 15 17256741

Girobank Trans cash
Girobank plc Bootle Merseyside GIR 0AA

Payslip

Inland Revenue

Year 2004-02

Net Income Tax ▶

Net National Insurance ▶

bank giro credit

Period ending **05 AUG 2004**
Payable by **19 AUG 2004**

159
209

24

792 PK 2042 0101 09

Reference J PAGE

110 5167

Credit account number

£

Amount due (no fee payable at PO counter)
CHEQUE ACCEPTABLE

By transfer from Alliance & Leicester Giro account number

For official use only

Cashier's stamp and initials

Signature ______________________

Date ______________

BANK OF ENGLAND
HEAD OFFICE COLLECTION A/C
INLAND REVENUE

CASH

CHEQUE

£

060159 014097

P30B(New)
BMSD 10/99

10-51-67

Please do not fold this payslip or write or mark below this line

SPECIMEN 792PK0000204201090 &7241105167 000000000 74 X

PETTY CASH BOOK

Receipts	Date	Details	Voucher No.	Payment	Analysis columns					
					VAT	Postage	Stationery	Office Expenses	Petrol/ diesel	Travel Expenses
£				£	£	£	£	£	£	£
200.00	2004 1 Aug	Balance b/f								

PETTY CASH VOUCHER No *800*

Date *1 August 2004*

	£	p
Computer disks	*107*	*86*
	107	*86*

Signature *B Shaw* Authorised

PETTY CASH VOUCHER No *801*

Date *1 August 2004*

	£	p
Stamps	*9*	*50*
	9	*50*

Signature *B Shaw* Authorised

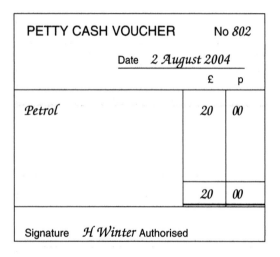

PETTY CASH VOUCHER No *802*

Date *2 August 2004*

	£	p
Petrol	*20*	*00*
	20	*00*

Signature *H Winter* Authorised

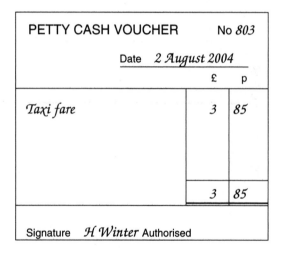

PETTY CASH VOUCHER No *803*

Date *2 August 2004*

	£	p
Taxi fare	*3*	*85*
	3	*85*

Signature *H Winter* Authorised

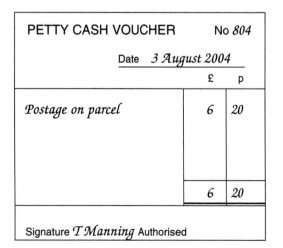

PETTY CASH VOUCHER No *804*

Date *3 August 2004*

	£	p
Postage on parcel	*6*	*20*
	6	*20*

Signature *T Manning* Authorised

PETTY CASH VOUCHER No *805*

Date *1 August 2004*

	£	p
Tea and coffee	*5*	*60*
	5	*60*

Signature *L Klein* Authorised

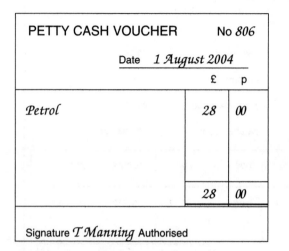

PETTY CASH VOUCHER No *806*

Date *1 August 2004*

	£	p
Petrol	*28*	*00*
	28	*00*

Signature *T Manning* Authorised

PETTY CASH VOUCHER No *807*

Date *2 August 2004*

	£	p
Envelopes	*11*	*25*
	11	*25*

Signature *L Klein* Authorised

PETTY CASH VOUCHER No *808*

Date *1 August 2004*

	£	p
Window cleaning	*8*	*00*
	8	*00*

Signature *B Shaw* Authorised

PETTY CASH VOUCHER No *809*

Date *2 August 2004*

	£	p
Taxi fare	*11*	*28*
	11	*28*

Signature *J Osborne* Authorised

supporting documents . . .

INVOICE

COMPUTER SUPPLIES LIMITED

16 HARLEY WAY MANCHESTER M3 6BY
Tel 0161 429 5314 Fax 0161 429 5951 Email toni@cool.u-net.com
VAT Reg GB 0745 4672 71

invoice to

Frontpage Stationery
Unit 2, Hillside Trading Estate
Knightwick
MR6 7LP

invoice no	2714
account	3993
your reference	47609
date/tax point	01 08 04

product code	description	quantity	price	unit	total	discount %	net
244	Zipo computer disks HD, PC formatted	18	5.10	box	91.80	0.00	91.80

terms
Payable on delivery

goods total	91.80
VAT	16.06
TOTAL	107.86

POST OFFICE	Receipt
Stamps	*£9.50*
TOTAL	*£9.50*

HYLTON FUEL
Hylton Road, Worcester WR2 5GN
VAT Reg 101 7543 26

22 litres unleaded	20.00
Cash tendered	20.00

02.08.04 14.23

purchase by a sales representative

Maxi Minicabs
Enstone Road, Martley, MR2 4JL

RECEIVED £ *3.85*

VAT Reg 229 7543 26

taxi to work when car would not start

POST OFFICE	**Receipt**
Parcel postage	*£6.20*
TOTAL	*£6.20*

VALUE FOODSTORE
23 JOHN STREET WYTHENFORD

Tea	2.70
Coffee	2.90
Total	5.60
Cash tendered	10.00
Change	4.40

01.08.04 10.30

Phil Johns, Windowcleaning
23 Garden Road, Sapley, MR9 4GF

RECEIVED £ *8.00*

Phil Johns is not registered for VAT

Star Stationery
Deansgate, Mereford MR1 3RT
VAT Reg 333 7804 01

02.08.04 09.30

200 envelopes C4	11.25
Total	11.25
Cash tendered	12.00
Change	00.75

Maxi Minicabs
Enstone Road, Martley, MR2 4JL

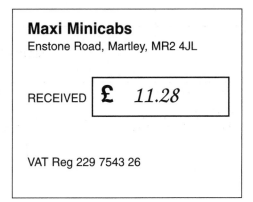

RECEIVED £ *11.28*

VAT Reg 229 7543 26

taxi to railway station for business trip

PURCHASES DAY BOOK

Date 2004	Details	Invoice No	Total £ p	VAT £ p	Net £ p
23 Jul	Sheppard & Suckling	2654	481.56	71.72	409.84
23 Jul	Drysdale & Co	2657	179.23	26.35	152.88
23 Jul	Nogan Limited	489	455.37	67.82	387.55
24 Jul	Meara Limited	407	1,438.91	214.30	1,224.61
24 Jul	Drysdale & Co	2684	229.21	33.70	195.51
24 Jul	Furlong Limited	7671	1,009.32	150.32	859.00
24 Jul	Putney Limited	3434	699.87	104.23	595.64

PURCHASES RETURNS DAY BOOK

Date 2004	Details	Credit Note No	Total £ p	VAT £ p	Net £ p
23 Jul	Soloman Limited	854	115.62	17.22	98.40
23 Jul	Meara Limited	415	78.30	11.66	66.64
24 Jul	Nogan Limited	103	104.45	15.55	88.90

MAIN (GENERAL) LEDGER

Purchases

Date 2004	Details	Amount £ p	Date 2004	Details	Amount £ p
23 Jul	Balance b/d	194,246.55			

Purchases returns

Date 2004	Details	Amount £ p	Date 2004	Details	Amount £ p
			23 Jul	Balance b/d	6,274.83

Purhases Ledger Control

Date 2004	Details	Amount £ p	Date 2004	Details	Amount £ p
			23 Jul	Balance b/d	35,201.26

Value Added Tax

Date 2004	Details	Amount £ p	Date 2004	Details	Amount £ p
			23 Jul	Balance b/d	8,321.35

Discount received

Date 2004	Details	Amount £ p	Date 2004	Details	Amount £ p
			23 Jul	Balance b/d	354.61

Cash Book: Payments

Date 2004	Details	Discount received £ p	Cash £ p	Bank £ p

MAIN LEDGER (continued)

Wages & salaries

Date 2004	Details	Amount £ p	Date 2004	Details	Amount £ p
23 Jul	Balance b/d	24,784.30			

Inland Revenue

Date 2004	Details	Amount £ p	Date 2004	Details	Amount £ p
			23 Jul	Balance b/d	846.00

Pension fund

Date 2004	Details	Amount £ p	Date 2004	Details	Amount £ p
			23 Jul	Balance b/d	164.00

Wages & salaries control

Date 2004	Details	Amount £ p	Date 2004	Details	Amount £ p

SUBSIDIARY (PURCHASES) LEDGER

Drysdale & Co

Date 2004	Details	Amount £ p	Date 2004	Details	Amount £ p

Furlong Limited

Date 2004	Details	Amount £ p	Date 2004	Details	Amount £ p
			23 Jul	Balance b/d	954.28

Meara Limited

Date 2004	Details	Amount £ p	Date 2004	Details	Amount £ p
			23 Jul	Balance b/d	3,390.86

Nogan Limited

Date 2004	Details	Amount £ p	Date 2004	Details	Amount £ p
			23 Jul	Balance b/d	1,974.26

Putney Limited

Date 2004	Details	Amount £ p	Date 2004	Details	Amount £ p
			23 Jul	Balance b/d	807.54

Sheppard & Suckling

Date 2004	Details	Amount £ p	Date 2004	Details	Amount £ p
			23 Jul	Balance b/d	98.45

Soloman Limited

Date 2004	Details	Amount £ p	Date 2004	Details	Amount £ p
			23 Jul	Balance b/d	756.81

Unit 2
Making and recording payments

Simulation 4: Amica Printing Company

(adapted from AAT sample material)

NVQ Element coverage

2.1 process documents relating to goods and services received

2.2 process payments

Scenario and contents

This Simulation is based on Amica Printing Company, a business employing twenty people, which prints brochures and leaflets for businesses and public sector organisations. The tasks in the Simulation include:

- checking, coding and approval of suppliers' invoices
- checking, coding and approval of suppliers' credit notes
- making payment by cheque and remittance advice on receipt of suppliers' statements
- paying employees on the payroll
- keeping accounting records up-to-date
- making petty cash payments
- handling and recording of cash

Suggested time allocation: three hours plus fifteen minutes reading time

SIMULATION 4
AMICA PRINTING COMPANY

SITUATION

You are Hei Lam Cheng, Accounts Assistant at Amica Printing Company, a business situated in the town of Wantage. Your duties include accounting for purchases on credit, making payments and controlling petty cash. You report to Alex Cook, the Accountant. The business is owned by Sam Fisher.

Amica Printing Company prints brochures and leaflets for businesses and public sector organisations in the UK.

The company employs 20 people, most of whom work in the printing factory. The Factory Supervisor is Henry Lynch, who reports to Edward Hunt, the Factory Manager. Nearly all the factory staff are employed on a permanent basis, but there are two temporary factory staff to whom special payroll procedures apply. All staff are paid monthly by bankers automated clearing system (BACS), unless they do not have a bank account, in which case they are paid in cash.

ACCOUNTING SYSTEM

Amica Printing Company operates a main ledger, which contains the Cash Book, the Petty Cash Book and the Purchase Ledger Control Account.

Each supplier has a separate account in the subsidiary (purchases) ledger, which is not part of the double-entry system. The company is registered for VAT.

Today's date is Tuesday 23 September 2003.

PART 1: TASKS 1 – 4

PROCESSING DOCUMENTS RELATING TO GOODS AND SERVICES RECEIVED

Suggested time 90 minutes

HANDLING PURCHASE INVOICES

You are responsible for processing documents relating to goods and services received.

Most of Amica Printing Company's purchases are made via the internet. You match invoices received to the following supporting documentation: the supplier master file, printouts of Amica Printing Company purchase orders, delivery notes from the supplier, and Amica Printing Company goods received notes (for factory purchases only).

If an invoice does not agree with the supporting documentation, the discrepancy is discussed initially with either Edward Hunt, the Factory Manager, or Alex Cook, the Accountant. If appropriate, the invoice is recorded once it has been signed by one of them to show that the discrepancy has been resolved.

For any other type of error, the invoice is not recorded but is returned to the supplier with a letter from you on headed notepaper, requesting a corrected invoice.

1 Refer to the invoices on pages 262 – 273 and the supporting documentation on pages 251 – 257. The last invoice recorded in the Purchase Day Book was numbered 6069.

Check each invoice against the supporting documentation, and check all the calculations, including settlement discount and VAT (which should always be rounded down to the nearest penny). Remember that any settlement (cash) discount is deducted first when calculating VAT. Where appropriate, mark any errors or discrepancies next to each invoice, and state the action to be taken.

Allocate an invoice number to each invoice that can be recorded, and write the relevant number in the space next to each document.

If it is appropriate, prepare notes for conversations with Edward Hunt or Alex Cook. Use page 273.

If it is appropriate, prepare letters to suppliers. Use the letterheads on pages 274 and 275.

HANDLING CREDIT NOTES

Credit notes must be agreed to goods returned notes, which are prepared by Edward Hunt.

A credit note which does not agree to the goods returned note is discussed with either Edward Hunt or Alex Cook, as appropriate. If the discrepancy is resolved by this method, the credit note is recorded once one of them has signed it.

For any other type of error, the credit note is not recorded, but is returned to the supplier with a letter from you on headed notepaper, requesting a corrected credit note.

2 Refer to the credit notes on pages 276 – 278 and the supporting documentation on pages 251, 252 and 258. The last credit note recorded in the Purchase Returns Day Book was numbered 276.

Check each credit note against the supporting documentation, and check all the calculations, including discount and VAT (which should always be rounded down to the nearest penny). Where appropriate, mark any errors or discrepancies beneath each credit note, and state the action to be taken.

Allocate a credit note number to each credit note to be recorded, and write the relevant number in the space provided next to each document.

If you have found any error relating to the supporting documentation, prepare notes for conversations with either Edward Hunt or Alex Cook. Use page 273.

If you have found any other errors, prepare a letter to the relevant supplier. Use the letterhead on page 280.

3 For all invoices and credit notes in Task 1 and 2 that have not been queried with Edward Hunt or Alex Cook, and so can be recorded, enter and analyse the details of invoices in the Purchase Day Book, and of credit notes in the Purchase Returns Day Book on pages 281 – 282.

4 Total the columns in the Purchase Day Book and the Purchase Returns Day Book.

Enter the relevant main ledger and subsidiary (purchase) ledger account codes in the Day Books in preparation for posting. Show which sides of the accounts will be posted by writing either `DR` or `CR` as appropriate.

Make the required entries in the main ledger and subsidiary (purchase) ledger accounts on pages 283 – 288.

Note: There are transactions already shown on some of the ledger accounts. You do NOT need to balance any ledger accounts after you have made your entries.

PART 2: TASKS 5 - 10

PROCESS PAYMENTS

Suggested time 90 minutes

PAYMENTS TO SUPPLIERS AND OTHERS

Twice a month you prepare cheque runs and BACS payments to be received by the payee on the second Friday and the last Friday of each month (the payment date). If settlement discount is available on any invoices at the payment date in question, you always take it. Otherwise, you take the maximum credit available according to the supplier's terms at the payment date. When assessing whether settlement discount is still available, you should treat the payment date for suppliers this week as 26 September 2003, as this is the date that cheques and BACS payments will be received by suppliers. The next payment date after the present one will be Friday 10 October 2003.

5 Refer to the supplier's statements on pages 289 – 292. Alex Cook has made a note on each statement of which invoices should be paid and how much settlement discount should be taken.

Check the statements against the relevant ledger accounts on pages 287 – 288. On the ledger accounts, tick each item that is due for payment. Beneath each statement, write any settlement discount that is available. Also make a note of any discrepancies, and the action to be taken about them.

Complete the remittance advices on pages 293 – 294 for all payments to suppliers that will be made. You do not need to fill in the supplier's address.

Refer to the cheque requisitions on pages 258 and 259 and check them against the supporting documentation on page 259. Make notes on page 295 as to what further action is required, if any.

Write up the Cash Book (Payments side) on page 296 with the amounts to be paid to suppliers and others today. In the Folio column, write the documentation that supports each payment.

Note: The BACS and cheque payments will be prepared later. You do not need to fill in relevant cheque numbers, and main and subsidiary (purchases) account numbers, nor total the Cash Book (Payments side), at this stage.

PAYROLL PAYMENTS

All staff are paid monthly in arrears on the last Friday of the month for the four (sometimes five) weeks ending the previous Friday. All factory staff are paid for a basic working week of 37.5 hours, plus overtime pay at time-and-a-half for hours over 37.5 hours per week. They can also receive occasional bonuses.

A payroll bureau, PrintPay Ltd, calculates gross pay and deductions and prepares payslips for all staff, and makes BACS payments by autopay to all permanent staff. You are sent a Factory Payroll with all amounts for permanent factory staff already inserted, plus payslips for temporary factory staff. Overtime and bonuses for temporary factory staff are listed on your Factory Pay List, which is signed by Edward Hunt and Alex Cook. You check this against the payslips, and then make the payments to any temporary factory staff from the payslips by cheque.

You raise queries about gross pay for temporary factory staff with Edward Hunt in person, and about the calculation and preparation of payslips with Robert Kane at PrintPay Ltd by phone.

You complete the Factory Payroll from the temporary factory staff payslips. Except where there is an error in the calculation of net pay you always include payslips for temporary staff in the Factory Payroll.

6 Check the payslips of the temporary factory staff shown on pages 297 and 298 against the Factory Pay List and Employee Master File on page 260. Makes notes beneath any payslip which contains an error or discrepancy, and state the action to be taken.

Check the calculation of net pay on the payslips of each of the temporary staff.

Note: You do not need to check how the PAYE and NIC figures, and the year to date figures, are calculated, so you do not need tax tables to perform this task.

Write up the Factory Payroll on page 299 for the temporary factory staff payslips, indicating the amounts to be paid by cheque.

Write up the Cash Book (payments side) on page 296 with the amounts to be paid to individual temporary factory staff by cheque.

Write up the Cash Book (payments side) for the total BACS payments by autopay that have been made by PrintPay Ltd to permanent factory staff.

Note: You need not fill in the references, nor total the Cash Book (payments side), at this stage.

7 Refer to the email from Henry Lynch, the Factory Supervisor, on page 260.

Draft an email to Henry in response to his memo, outlining the course of action you need to take. Use page 300.

PETTY CASH PAYMENTS

Each day you are responsible for writing up Petty Cash vouchers from valid receipts for the expenditure paid out. Receipts are only valid if signed by the recipient and authorised by Alex Cook. Employees can only make petty cash claims up to £40. If they wish to claim for more than this amount, they are required to fill out an expenses claim form. You top up the petty cash to £300 each time the amount of cash in the petty cash box falls below £60.

8 Refer to the list of ledger accounts on page 251 and the authorised receipts on page 261.

Complete vouchers on page 301, calculating VAT as appropriate (round VAT down to the nearest penny), for all receipts that you are able to pay from petty cash.

Make notes on page 302 on why you have not prepared a voucher for all the receipts.

Refer to the list of notes and coin in the petty cash box on page 302. On this list, write in what notes and coin are being paid out in respect of the valid receipts. You should use the highest denominations of notes and coin that are available. Then calculate a revised total for notes and coin in the petty cash box.

Note: You can assume that the cash has now been paid to the recipients.

Write up the Petty Cash Book on page 303 for the vouchers you have prepared and paid, analysing the expenditure.

Total the Petty Cash Book and calculate the balance. Ensure that the Petty Cash Book balance agrees with the amount of cash in the petty cash box which you have just calculated.

Calculate any necessary top-up for petty cash and include the payment for this in the Cash Book (payments side) on page 296. You do not need to fill in the cheque number at this stage.

Enter the relevant main ledger codes in the Petty Cash Book in preparation for posting to the main ledger.

Write up the Petty Cash Book for the top-up and calculate the balance at the end of the day.

Note: You may assume that all the payments you have listed out in the Cash Book (payments side) have been authorised by Alex Cook on behalf of Sam Fisher.

9 Complete the bank giro credit form on the supplier's statement on page 290 and write out a cheque on page 304 for the amount due. This will be signed by Sam Fisher.

Complete the cheques on pages 304 – 306 for all the other items that you have written up in the Cash Book (payments side). These will be signed by Sam Fisher.

Enter the cheque numbers in the Cash Book (payments side).

Total the Cash Book (payments side) and insert the relevant main and subsidiary (purchase) ledger codes in preparation for posting to the ledgers.

10 From the Cash Book (payments side), the Payroll and the Petty Cash Book, make the appropriate entries in the ledger accounts on pages 283 – 288

Calculate the balance on the Purchase Ledger Control Account in the main ledger, and on all the subsidiary ledger accounts. Show also the balance brought down on 24 September for each of these accounts.

DATA

The following are extracts from the lists of ledger codes:

MAIN LEDGER

Ledger account	**Ledger code**
Administration	090
Cash book	100
Purchase ledger control account	110
Discount received	120
Factory wages control	130
Factory wages expense	140
PAYE/NIC creditor	150
Petty cash book	160
Postage	170
Production expenses	180
Purchases	190
Purchases returns	200
Stationery	210
VAT	220

SUBSIDIARY (PURCHASES) LEDGER

Ledger account	**Ledger code**
Abingdon Paper Ltd	1101
Feltham Bindery Ltd	1102
Hamburg Print Plates Ltd	1103
Ilsley Inks Ltd	1104
Sidney Stationers	1105
Wantage Engineering Ltd	1106

SUPPLIER MASTER FILE: SUBSIDIARY (PURCHASES) LEDGER				
account code	*supplier name*	*trade discount %*	*settlement terms*	*payment method*
1101	Abingdon Paper Ltd	5	30 days net	Cheque
1102	Feltham Bindery Ltd	0	30 days net	Cheque
1103	Hamburg Print Plates Ltd	0	3% 7 days 30 days net	BACS*
1104	Ilsley Inks Ltd	5	30 days net	Cheque
1105	Sidney Stationers	0	30 days net	Cheque
1106	Wantage Engineering Ltd	10	1% 21 days 30 days net	Cheque

* Hamburg Print Plates Limited is paid by BACS: Account no 67461313, sort code 80-16-74

HAMBURG PRINT PLATES LTD

Price list

Plate for:	**£ (each)**
Hamburg 250 print press	25.00
Hamburg 500 print press	30.00
Hamburg 1000 print press	35.00
Myobi 400 press	20.00
Myobi 600 press	37.50
Myobi 800 press	50.00

Amica Printing Company

McLaren Trading Estate, Wantage OX12 8SD Tel: 01235 687465

INTERNET PURCHASE ORDER

To:Abingdon Paper Ltd, Milton Park, Abingdon, Oxon OX13 9AS

Description of item(s) ordered	*Quantity*	*Price from website (£)*
100gsm Nordic White A1 (500kg) pack	5	200.00
260gsm Polar Ice A1 (500kg pack)	4	350.00

Ordered: *Edward Hunt* Date: *15 September 2003*

Expense classified as: *Purchases*

Abingdon Paper Ltd

Milton Park, Abingdon, Oxon OX13 9AS Tel: 01235 412233

DELIVERY NOTE

To:Amica Printing Company, McLaren Trading Estate, Wantage OX12 8SD

Description of item(s)	**Quantity**	
100gsm Nordic White A1 (500kg pack)	5	
260gsm Polar Ice A1 (500kg pack)	4	

Signed for by: *Edward Hunt* Date: *22 September 2003*

Amica Printing Company

GOODS RECEIVED NOTE

From: Abingdon Paper Ltd

Description	*Quantity*	*Received in good condition?*
100gsm Nordic White A1 (500kg pack)	5	Yes
260gsm Polar Ice A1 (500kg pack)	4	Yes

Signed: *Edward Hunt* Date: *22 September 2003*

Amica Printing Company

McLaren Trading Estate, Wantage OX12 8SD, Tel: 01235 687465

PURCHASE ORDER

To:Feltham Bindery Ltd, Chertsey Road Trading Estate, Feltham, Middx TW12 5AB

Description of item(s) ordered	*Quantity*	*price agreed (£)*
Consultancy report on installation of a fully automated binding line at the Wantage factory	1	3,250.00 plus VAT

Signed: Sam Fisher

Date: 2 September 2003

Expense classified as: Production expenses

Lam,

I've received this report now so you can pay the bill when it comes in.

Sam

19 September 2003

Amica Printing Company

McLaren Trading Estate, Wantage OX12 8SD, Tel: 01235 687465

INTERNET PURCHASE ORDER

To:Hamburg Print Plates Ltd, Highgrove Road, Newbury, Berks NY9 4BW

Description of item(s) ordered	*Quantity*	
Hamburg 250 print press plates	100	
Hamburg 1000 print press plates	50	
Myobi 600 press plates	70	

Ordered: *Edward Hunt* Date: *18 September 2003*

Expense classified as: *Purchases*

Hamburg Print Plates Ltd

Highgrove Road, Newbury, Berks NY9 4BW

DELIVERY NOTE

To: Amica Printing Company, McLaren Trading Estate, Wantage OX12 8SD

Description of item(s)	**Quantity**	
Myobi 600 press plates	70	
Hamburg 1000 print press plates	50	
Hamburg 250 print press plates	100	

Signed for by: *Edward Hunt* Date: *22 September 2003*

Amica Printing Company

GOODS RECEIVED NOTE

From: Hamburg Print Plates Ltd

Description	*Quantity*	*Received in good condition?*
Myobi 600 press plates	70	Yes
Hamburg 1000 print press plates	50	Yes
Hamburg 250 print press plates	100	Yes

Signed: *Edward Hunt* Date: *22 September 2003*

Amica Printing Company

McLaren Trading Estate, Wantage OX12 8SD Tel: 01235 687465

PURCHASE ORDER

To:Sidney Stationers, 40 Market Square, Wantage OX12 5KK

Description of item(s) ordered	*Quantity*	*price agreed (£)*
Red A4 lever arch files	200	1.49

Ordered: *Alex Cook* Date: *16 September 2003*

Expense classified as: *Stationery*

Sidney Stationers Ltd

40 Market Square, Wantage OX12 5KK

DELIVERY NOTE

To:Amica Printing Company, McLaren Trading Estate, Wantage OX12 8SD

Description of item(s)	**Quantity**	
Red A4 lever arch files	200	

Signed for by: *Alex Cook* Date: *22 September 2003*

Amica Printing Company

McLaren Trading Estate, Wantage OX12 8SD Tel: 01235 687465

INTERNET PURCHASE ORDER

To:Wantage Engineering Ltd, Grove Road, Wantage OX12 7SM

Description of item(s) ordered	*Quantity*	*website price (£)*
Machine oil	10 litres	5.00/litre
Print press cleaning fluid	50 litres	6.50/litre
Press tester units	25	15.00 each

Ordered: *Edward Hunt* Date: *15 September 2003*

Expense classified as: *Purchases*

Wantage Engineering Ltd

Grove Road, Wantage OX12 7SM

DELIVERY NOTE

To:Amica Printing Company, McLaren Trading Estate, Wantage OX12 8SD

Description of item(s)	Quantity	
Print press cleaning fluid	50 litres	
Machine oil	10 litres	
Press tester units	25	

Agreed by: *Edward Hunt* Date: *22 September 2003*

Amica Printing Company

GOODS RECEIVED NOTE

From: Wantage Engineering Ltd

Description	Quantity	Received in good condition?
Print press cleaning fluid	50 litres	Yes
Machine oil	10 litres	Yes
Press tester units	25	Yes

Signed: *Edward Hunt* Date: *22 September 2003*

Amica Printing Company

GOODS RETURNED NOTE

From: Hamburg Print Plates Ltd

Description	*Quantity*
Hamburg 500 print press plates	5

Reason for return:

On inspection these plates are damaged and cannot be used in the printing machines

Signed: *Edward Hunt* Date: *15 September 2003*

Return classified as: *Purchases returns*

Amica Printing Company

GOODS RETURNED NOTE

From: Ilsley Inks Ltd

Description	*Quantity*
Special order ink pantone colour 291	10 kilos – ordered at £25.00 per kilo

Reason for return

On examination, the ink is not the correct pantone colour and cannot be used.

Signed: *Edward Hunt* Date: *15 September 2003*

Return classified as: *Purchases returns*

Amica Printing Company

CHEQUE REQUISITION

Date:	22 September 2003
Payee:	Yarnton Estates Ltd
Amount:	£150.00 + VAT
Supporting documentation:	To follow
Expense classified as:	

Signed: Henry Lynch, Factory Supervisor

Amica Printing Company

CHEQUE REQUISITION

Date:	22 September 2003
Payee:	Children in Need
Amount:	£300
Supporting documentation:	This is the amount that our Pudsey Bear campaign raised. Please see the memo attached.
Expense classified as:	Administration

Signed: Alex Cook, Accountant

MEMO

To:	All staff members
From:	Sam Fisher
Subject:	Children in Need – Pudsey Bear campaign
Date:	19 September 2003

As you all know, we spent a very productive and enjoyable day this week doing silly things to help the Pudsey Bear campaign raise funds for Children in Need. I said to you that I would donate £300 to Children in Need if the day proved a success. I'm delighted that it exceeded even my expectations, so I'm happy to donate the £300.

I'd like to thank all those who took part.

Sam Fisher

NOTE

Alex

Please issue a cheque for £300, and analyse it to Administration.

Sam

19 September 2003

NOTE

to Admin

Please display copies of this on all Notice Boards until 15 October.

Thanks

Sam Fisher

Amica Printing Company

Factory Pay List – Temporary Factory Workers

Date: 23 September 2003

Four weeks ending: 19 September 2003

Name	*Basic hours*	*Overtime hours*	*Bonus*
Pippa Allen	150.00	12	£15.00
Usha Gupta	37.50	4	£5.00

Signed: *Edward Hunt* Authorised: Alex Cook

Amica Printing Company

Employee Master File – Temporary Factory Workers

Name	*Employee number*	*NI Number*	*Tax code*	*Basic hourly rate (£)*	*Pay by*
Pippa Allen	FT683	KS820192M	475L	5.50	Cheque
Usha Gupta	FT685	WL293048P	475L	5.50	Cheque

EMAIL

To: heilamcheng@amica.co.uk

From: henrylynch@amica.co.uk

CC:

Subject: Larry Haynes

Date: 22 September 2003

Message

Hi Lam

Larry approached me yesterday to say that he has recently applied for a mortgage and the lender needs confirmation of his pay and benefits, plus copies of his last three payslips. He hasn't kept any of the documentation we have given him in the past on these matters, so I said I would get hold of copies and go through any queries he may have about them with him in person. Please leave these on my desk in the factory first thing tomorrow.

Henry

POST OFFICE LTD

Mon 22 September 2003

Special Delivery

2 @ £18.95	37.90
2 @ £6.50	13.00
Total due to Post Office	50.90
Cash from customer	50.90
Balance	0.00

Dispatch of leaflets to customers

Martha Collins 23 Sep 03

Approved: Alex Cook

Larkhill Stationers

VAT 0576761338

Stapler (inc VAT)	6.99
Total	6.99
Cash tendered	10.00
Change amount	3.01

Date 22 Sept 2003 Time 09.17

Office stapler to replace missing stapler in factory

Edward Hunt

Approved: Alex Cook

Sparkbrook Tools

VAT 9870257119

Mon 22 September 2003

5" spanner	15.99
Total due (inc VAT)	15.99
Cash from customer	20.00
Change	4.01

Urgent purchase for factory,

Larry Haynes

Approved: Alex Cook

ANSWER PAGES

INVOICE

Abingdon Paper Limited

Milton Park, Abingdon, Oxon OX13 9AS

Tel 01235 412233
Fax 01235 412866

VAT Reg 917 569 87 45

customer:
Amica Printing Company
McLaren Trading Estate
Wantage
OX12 8SD

invoice no. 45472

date 22 September 2003

quantity	description	Price (£)	Total (£)
5	100 gsm Nordic White A1	200.00	1,000.00
4	260 gsm Polar Ice A1	350.00	1,400.00
		Goods total	2,400.00
		Less trade discount 5%	120.00
		Subtotal	2,280.00
		VAT at 17.5%	399.00
		Invoice total	2,679.00

Terms: 30 days net

Invoice number allocated ....

Errors or discrepancies..

....

....

Action to be taken..

....

....

INVOICE

Feltham Bindery Limited

Chertsey Road Trading Estate, Feltham
Middlesex TW12 5AB

Tel/Fax 020 8371 5987

VAT Reg 687 368 73 44

customer:
Amica Printing Company
McLaren Trading Estate
Wantage
OX12 8SD

invoice no. 7631

date 22 September 2003

description	**Price (£)**	**Total (£)**
Consultancy report on installation of fully automated binding line, as per Sam Fisher's purchase order of 2 September 2003, and conversation with Alex Cook	4,250.00	4,250.00
	Subtotal	4,250.00
	Trade discount 0%	0.00
	Subtotal	4,250.00
	VAT at 17.5%	743.75
	Invoice total	4,993.75

Terms: 30 days net

Invoice number allocated ....

Errors or discrepancies..

....

....

Action to be taken..

....

....

INVOICE

Hamburg Print Plates Limited

Highgrove Road, Newbury, Berks NY9 4BW

Tel 01461 476431
Fax 01461 547643

VAT Reg 0547351034

customer:
Amica Printing Company
McLaren Trading Estate
Wantage
OX12 8SD

invoice no. 29073

date 22 September 2003

quantity	description	Price (£)	Total (£)
70	Myobi 600 press plates	37.50	2,625.00
50	Hamburg 1000 print press plates	35.00	1,750.00
100	Hamburg 250 print press plates	25.00	2,500.00

Goods total	6,875.00
Less trade discount 0%	0.00
Subtotal	6,875.00
VAT at 17.5%	1,167.03
Invoice total	8,042.03

Terms: Cash (settlement) discount*: 3% for payment in 7 days, otherwise 30 days net

£206.25

Invoice number allocated ....

Errors or discrepancies..

....

....

Action to be taken..

....

....

INVOICE

Ilsley Inks Limited

Ridgeway House, East Ilsley, Berks NY7 1LS

Tel: 01461 7576764 Fax: 01461 343463

VAT Reg 0917757537

customer:
Amica Printing Company
McLaren Trading Estate
Wantage
OX12 8SD

invoice no. 19873

date 22 September 2003

quantity	description	Price (£)	Total (£)
15kg	Cyan ink for Hamburg colour presses	20.00	300.00
20kg	Yellow ink for Myobi presses	12.50	250.00

Subtotal	550.00
Trade discount 5%	27.50
Subtotal	522.50
VAT at 17.5%	91.43
Invoice total	613.93

Terms: 30 days net

Invoice number allocated ....

Errors or discrepancies..

....

....

Action to be taken..

....

....

INVOICE

Sidney Stationers Limited

40 Market Square, Wantage OX12 5KK

Tel: 01235 497611 Fax: 01235 576643

VAT Reg 1473658734

customer:
Amica Printing Company
McLaren Trading Estate
Wantage
OX12 8SD

invoice no. 83195

date 22 September 2003

quantity	description	Price (£)	Total (£)
200	A4 lever arch files – red	1.49	298.00

Goods total	298.00
Trade discount 0%	0.00
Subtotal	298.00
VAT at 17.5%	52.15
Invoice total	350.15

Terms: strictly 30 days net

Invoice number allocated ....

Errors or discrepancies...

....

....

....

Action to be taken..

....

INVOICE

Wantage Engineering Limited

Grove Road, Wantage OX12 7SM

Tel: 01235 232155 Fax: 01235 235698

VAT Reg 4654646446

customer:
Amica Printing Company
McLaren Trading Estate
Wantage
OX12 8SD

invoice no. 699123

date 22 September 2003

quantity	description	Price (£)	Total (£)
50 litres	Print press cleaning fluid	6.50	250.00
10 litres	Machine oil	5.00	60.00
25	Press tester units	15.00	475.00
		Goods total	785.00
		Trade discount 10%	78.00
		Subtotal	707.00
		VAT at 17.5%	123.72
		Invoice total	830.72

Terms: Cash (settlement) discount: 1% for payment in 21 days, otherwise 30 days net

£7.07

Invoice number allocated ....

Errors or discrepancies..

....

....

....

Action to be taken...

....

Notes for conversation with Alex Cook

Notes for conversation with Edward Hunt

Amica Printing Company

McLaren Trading Estate, Wantage OX12 8SD

Tel: 01235 687465 Fax: 01235 687412

Amica Printing Company

McLaren Trading Estate, Wantage OX12 8SD

Tel: 01235 687465 Fax: 01235 687412

CREDIT NOTE

Hamburg Print Plates Limited

Highgrove Road, Newbury, Berks NY9 4BW

Tel 01461 476431
Fax 01461 547643

VAT Reg 0547351034

customer:

Amica Printing Company
McLaren Trading Estate
Wantage
OX12 8SD

credit note no. CN246

date 22 September 2003

quantity	description/code	Price (£)	Total (£)
5	Hamburg 500 print press plates	30.00	150.00

Goods total	150.00
Trade discount 0%	0.00
Sub-total	150.00
VAT at 17.5%	25.46
Credit note total	175.46

Reason for credit:
Damaged (part of batch delivered and invoiced 15 September 2003)

Reduce cash (settlement) discount on original invoice by £4.50

Credit note number allocated ....

Errors or discrepancies...

....

....

Action to be taken...

....

....

CREDIT NOTE

Ilsley Inks Limited

Ridgeway House, East Ilsley, Berks NY7 1LS

Tel 01461 7576764
Fax 01461 343463

VAT Reg 091 775 75 37

customer:

Amica Printing Company
McLaren Trading Estate
Wantage
OX12 8SD

credit note no. 1701

date 22 September 2003

quantity	description/code	Price (£)	Total (£)
10 kilos	Special order pantone ink 291	25.00	250.00

Goods total	250.00
Trade discount 5%	12.50
Sub-total	237.50
VAT at 17.5%	41.56
Credit note total	279.06

Reason for credit:
Incorrect pantone ink delivered and invoiced
15 September 2003

Credit note number allocated ....

Errors or discrepancies...

....

....

Action to be taken...

....

....

Amica Printing Company

McLaren Trading Estate, Wantage OX12 8SD

Tel: 01235 687465 Fax: 01235 687412

PURCHASES DAY BOOK **Folio PDB 30**

Date 2003	Supplier	Purchases ledger code	Invoice number allocated	Total £	VAT £	Purchases £	Stationery £
Total							
Main ledger codes							

PURCHASES RETURNS DAY BOOK							Folio PRDB 6
Date 2003	Supplier	Purchases ledger code	Credit note number allocated	Total £	VAT £	Purchases returns £	Stationery £
Total							
Main ledger codes							

MAIN LEDGER

100 ADMINISTRATION

Date 2003	Details	Folio	Amount £	Date 2003	Details	Folio	Amount £

110 PURCHASE LEDGER CONTROL ACCOUNT

Date 2003	Details	Folio	Amount £	Date 2003	Details	Folio	Amount £
				22 Sep	Balance b/d		7,186.79

120 DISCOUNT RECEIVED

Date 2003	Details	Folio	Amount £	Date 2003	Details	Folio	Amount £

MAIN LEDGER

130 FACTORY WAGES CONTROL

Date 2003	Details	Folio	Amount £	Date 2003	Details	Folio	Amount £

140 FACTORY WAGES EXPENSE

Date 2003	Details	Folio	Amount £	Date 2003	Details	Folio	Amount £

150 PAYE/NIC CREDITOR

Date 2003	Details	Folio	Amount £	Date 2003	Details	Folio	Amount £

MAIN LEDGER

170 POSTAGE

Date 2003	Details	Folio	Amount £	Date 2003	Details	Folio	Amount £

180 PRODUCTION EXPENSES

Date 2003	Details	Folio	Amount £	Date 2003	Details	Folio	Amount £

190 PURCHASES

Date 2003	Details	Folio	Amount £	Date 2003	Details	Folio	Amount £

MAIN LEDGER

200 PURCHASES RETURNS

Date 2003	Details	Folio	Amount £	Date 2003	Details	Folio	Amount £

210 STATIONERY

Date 2003	Details	Folio	Amount £	Date 2003	Details	Folio	Amount £

220 VAT

Date 2003	Details	Folio	Amount £	Date 2003	Details	Folio	Amount £

SUBSIDIARY (PURCHASES) LEDGER

1101 ABINGDON PAPER LTD

Date 2003	Details	Folio	Amount £	Date 2003	Details	Folio	Amount £
				2 Sep	Invoice 5980	PDB 27	2,511.56

1102 FELTHAM BINDERY LTD

Date 2003	Details	Folio	Amount £	Date 2003	Details	Folio	Amount £

1103 HAMBURG PRINT PLATES LTD

Date 2003	Details	Folio	Amount £	Date 2003	Details	Folio	Amount £
				5 Sep	Invoice 5982	PDB 27	1,017.68
				15 Sep	Invoice 6040	PDB 29	1,754.62

SUBSIDIARY (PURCHASES) LEDGER

1104 ILSLEY INKS LTD

Date 2003	Details	Folio	Amount £	Date 2003	Details	Folio	Amount £
				2 Sep	Invoice 5985	PDB 27	726.46
				15 Sep	Invoice 6042	PDB 29	1,088.34

1105 SIDNEY STATIONERS LTD

Date 2003	Details	Folio	Amount £	Date 2003	Details	Folio	Amount £
29 Aug	Credit note 250	PRDB 5	17.62	2 Sep	Invoice 5965	PDB 26	105.75

1106 WANTAGE ENGINEERING LTD

Date 2003	Details	Folio	Amount £	Date 2003	Details	Folio	Amount £

STATEMENT OF ACCOUNT

Abingdon Paper Limited

Milton Park, Abingdon OX13 9AS, Tel 01235 412233, Fax 01235 412866 VAT Reg 9175698745

Customer Amica Printing Company, McLaren Trading Estate, Wantage OX12 8SD

Date 22 September 2003

Date	Transaction	Debit £	Credit £	Balance £
2003				
1 Sep	Invoice	2,511.56 ✔		
22 Sep	Invoice	2,679.00		
Balance outstanding				5,190.56

Lam,
Please pay ticked item. Alex Cook.

Normal terms:
30 days.

Discount to be taken ....

Discrepancies..

....

....

Action to be taken..

....

....

STATEMENT OF ACCO

Hamburg Print Plates L

Highgrove Road, Newbury, Berks NY9 4BW, Tel 0146

VAT Reg 0547351034

Lam,
Please pay ticked items. Cash discount of £201.75 to be taken on invoice and credit note dated 22 September 03. Alex Cook.

Customer Amica Printing Company, McLaren Trad

Date 22 September 2003

Date	Transaction	Debit £	Credit £	Balance £
2003				
4 Sep	Invoice	1,017.68 ✔		
15 Sep	Invoice	1,754.62		
22 Sep	Credit note		175.46 ✔	
22 Sep	Invoice	8,042.03 ✔		

Balance outstanding 10,638.87

Normal terms: 3% settlement (cash) discount is available for payment within 7 days. Otherwise our terms are strictly net 30 days.

---

date ____________ paid in by ____________ **bank giro credit**

Cashier's stamp

Northeast Bank

Sort Code 80-16-74

Account Hamburg Print Plates Ltd

Account no 67461313

cash

cheques

£

Discount to be taken..

....

Discrepancies..

....

Action to be taken..

....

....

STATEMENT OF ACCOUNT

Ilsley Inks Limited

Ridgeway House, East Ilsley, Berks NY7 1LS
Tel 01461 7576764, Fax 01461 343463 VAT Reg 0917757537

Customer Amica Printing Company, McLaren Trading Estate, Wantage OX12 8SD

Date 22 September 2003

Date	**Transaction**	**Debit £**	**Credit £**	**Balance £**
2003				
1 Sep	Invoice	726.46 ✔		
22 Sep	Invoice	1,088.34		
22 Sep	Credit note		279.06	
Balance outstanding				1,535.74

Lam,
Please pay ticked item. Alex Cook.

Normal terms:
30 days.

Discount to be taken ....

Discrepancies ....

....

....

Action to be taken ....

....

....

STATEMENT OF ACCOUNT

Sidney Stationers Limited

40 Market Square, Wantage OX12 5KK
Tel 01235 497611, Fax 01235 576643 VAT Reg 1473658734

Customer Amica Printing Company, McLaren Trading Estate, Wantage OX12 8SD

Date 22 September 2003

Date	Transaction	Debit £	Credit £	Balance £
2003				
27 Aug	Invoice	105.75 ✔		
28 Aug	Credit note		17.62 ✔	
22 Sep	Invoice	350.15		
Balance outstanding				438.28

Lam,
Please pay ticked items. Alex Cook.

Normal terms:
30 days.

Discount to be taken ....

Discrepancies..

....

....

Action to be taken..

....

....

REMITTANCE ADVICE

Amica Printing Company

McLaren Trading Estate, Wantage OX12 8SD
Tel 01235 687465, Fax 01235 687412

Supplier
Subsidiary (purchase) ledger code:

Date	Transaction reference	Amount (£)

REMITTANCE ADVICE

Amica Printing Company

McLaren Trading Estate, Wantage OX12 8SD
Tel 01235 687465, Fax 01235 687412

Supplier
Subsidiary (purchase) ledger code:

Date	Transaction reference	Amount (£)

REMITTANCE ADVICE

Amica Printing Company

McLaren Trading Estate, Wantage OX12 8SD
Tel 01235 687465, Fax 01235 687412

Supplier
Subsidiary (purchase) ledger code:

Date	Transaction reference	Amount (£)

REMITTANCE ADVICE

Amica Printing Company

McLaren Trading Estate, Wantage OX12 8SD
Tel 01235 687465, Fax 01235 687412

Supplier
Subsidiary (purchase) ledger code:

Date	Transaction reference	Amount (£)

Notes re. Task 5

MAIN LEDGER: 100 CASH BOOK (PAYMENTS) CB 30

Date 2003	Details	Cheque number/ BACS ref	Folio	Payment £	Admin £	Factory wages £	Petty cash £	Suppliers £	Discount received £	Purchases ledger codes
Main ledger codes			DR							
			CR							

Amica Printing Company				
Employee: Pippa Allen	Employee no: FT683			
NI No: KS 82 01 92 M	Tax code: 475L		Date: 26 Sep 2003	Tax period: Mth 6
Pay for FOUR weeks ending: 19 September 2003	Hours	Rate (£)	AMOUNT (£)	YEAR TO DATE (£)
Basic hours	150.00	5.50	825.00	
Time and a half	12.00	8.25	99.00	
Bonus		15.00	15.00	
PAY FOR PERIOD			939.00	4,695.00
PAYE			149.93	899.57
Employee's NI (Employer's NI £61.28)			56.34	
TOTAL DEDUCTIONS			206.27	
NET PAY			732.73	

Errors or discrepancies..

....

Action to be taken..

Amica Printing Company

Employee: Usha Gupta	Employee no: FT685			
NI No: WL 29 30 48 P	Tax code: BR		Date: 26 Sep 2003	Tax period: Mth 6
Pay for FOUR weeks ending: 19 September 2003	Hours	Rate (£)	AMOUNT (£)	YEAR TO DATE (£)
Basic hours	37.50	5.50	206.25	
Time and a half	4.00	8.25	33.00	
Bonus		5.00	5.00	
PAY FOR PERIOD			244.25	244.25
PAYE			53.73	53.73
Employee's NI (Employer's NI £17.50)			14.65	
TOTAL DEDUCTIONS NET PAY			68.38 175.87	

Errors or discrepancies...

....

Action to be taken...

FACTORY PAYROLL MONTH 6

Employee	Employee number	Pay for period £	PAYE £	Employee's NIC £	Net pay £	Employer's NIC £
Temporary factory payroll total						
Permanent factory payroll total		5,014.96	1,002.99	351.04	3,660.93	347.77
Total factory payroll						
Main ledger codes	DR	140	130	130		140
	CR	130	150	150		150
Payment by BACS – permanent						
Payment by cheque						

EMAIL

from	henrylynch@amica.co.uk
to	heilamcheng@amica.co.uk
cc	
subject	
date	23 September 2003

message

petty cash voucher Number *099*

date

description	amount	

paid to ....

documentation ....

petty cash voucher Number *100*

date

description	amount	

paid to ....

documentation ....

petty cash voucher Number *101*

date

description	amount	

paid to ....

documentation ....

Note to Task 8

PETTY CASH LISTING

Notes and coin in box	In petty cash box as at 22 Sep 03 £	To be paid out 23 September 2003 Voucher number: £	Voucher number: £	Voucher number: £	In petty cash book as at 23 Sep 03 £
£50	0.00				
£20	40.00				
£10	20.00				
£5	15.00				
£2	0.00				
£1	3.00				
50p	1.50				
20p	1.00				
10p	0.20				
5p	0.10				
2p	0.04				
1p	0.04				
Total					

160 Petty Cash Book

PCB 30

Receipts £	Date 2003	Details	Voucher Number	Payments £	VAT £	Postage £	Production Expenses £	Stationery £
80.88	22 Sep	Balance b/d						
			Totals					
		Interim balance c/d						
		Interim balance b/d						
		End of day balance c/d						
Main ledger codes			DR					
			CR					

Oxbank PLC
Cornmarket, Oxford, OX1 4FG

date 13-45-65

Pay

Account payee only

only

£

AMICA PRINTING COMPANY

546610 134565 63500671

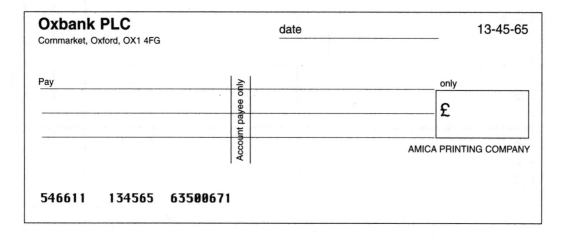

Oxbank PLC
Cornmarket, Oxford, OX1 4FG

date 13-45-65

Pay

Account payee only

only

£

AMICA PRINTING COMPANY

546611 134565 63500671

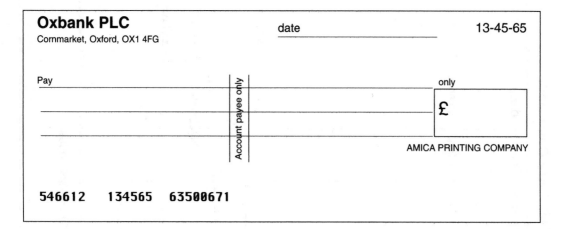

Oxbank PLC
Cornmarket, Oxford, OX1 4FG

date 13-45-65

Pay

Account payee only

only

£

AMICA PRINTING COMPANY

546612 134565 63500671

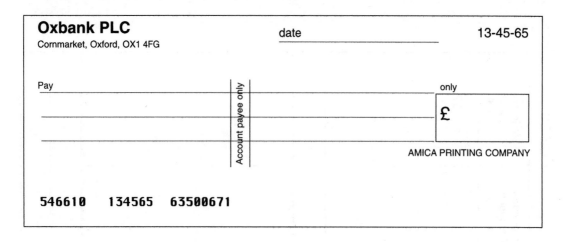

Oxbank PLC
Cornmarket, Oxford, OX1 4FG

date 13-45-65

Pay

Account payee only

only

£

AMICA PRINTING COMPANY

546613 134565 63500671

Oxbank PLC
Cornmarket, Oxford, OX1 4FG

date 13-45-65

Pay

Account payee only

only

£

AMICA PRINTING COMPANY

546614 134565 63500671

Oxbank PLC
Cornmarket, Oxford, OX1 4FG

date 13-45-65

Pay

Account payee only

only

£

AMICA PRINTING COMPANY

546615 134565 63500671

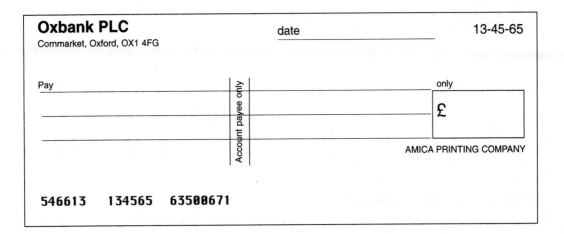

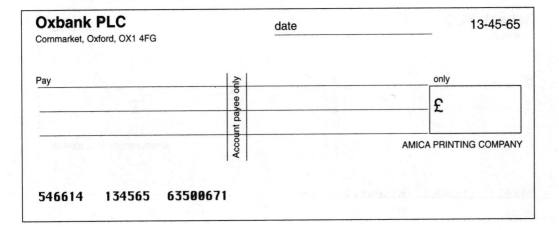

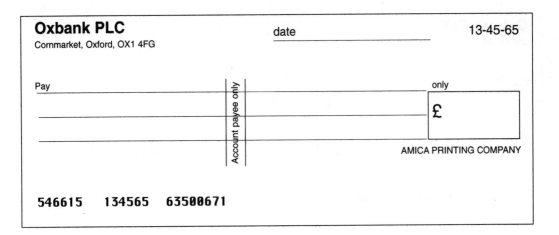

Oxbank PLC
Cornmarket, Oxford, OX1 4FG

date 13-45-65

Pay

Account payee only

only

£

AMICA PRINTING COMPANY

546616 134565 63500671

Oxbank PLC
Cornmarket, Oxford, OX1 4FG

date 13-45-65

Pay

Account payee only

only

£

AMICA PRINTING COMPANY

546617 134565 63500671

Oxbank PLC
Cornmarket, Oxford, OX1 4FG

date 13-45-65

Pay

Account payee only

only

£

AMICA PRINTING COMPANY

546618 134565 63500671

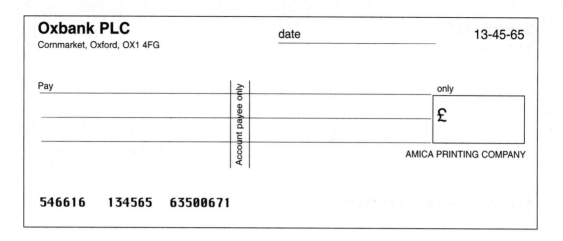

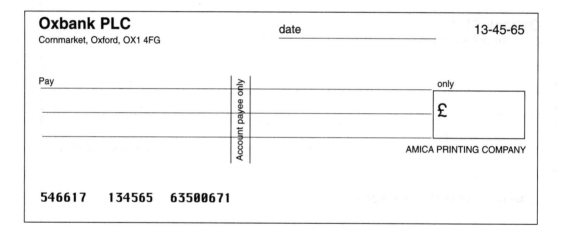

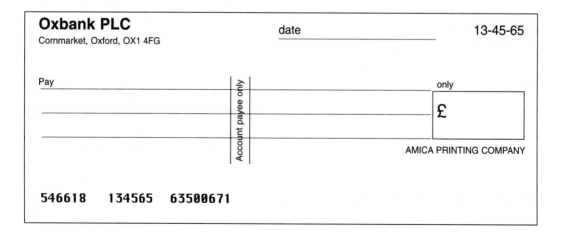

Unit 3
Preparing ledger balances and an initial trial balance

Simulation 5
Sunny Days Garden Products

NVQ Element coverage

3.1 bank balance transactions

3.2 prepare ledger balances and control accounts

3.3 draft an initial trial balance

Scenario and contents

This Simulation is based on 'Sunny Days', a business which buys garden furniture and equipment from manufacturers and sells to garden centres and specialist shops.

The tasks in the Simulation include:

- preparation of trial balances
- entering balances from the trial balance into accounts in the main ledger
- restoring the imprest amount of petty cash book, balancing the account, and reconciling the cash held
- checking the bank statement against the cash book for accuracy, updating the cash book as necessary, and preparing a bank reconciliation statement
- the operation of sales ledger and purchases ledger control accounts, and reconciling the balances with the subsidiary ledgers
- journal entries, including the correction of errors

Suggested time allocation: three hours and fifteen minutes reading time

SIMULATION 5
SUNNY DAYS GARDEN PRODUCTS

SITUATION

'Sunny Days' is a business which buys garden furniture and equipment from manufacturers and sells to garden centres and specialist shops. The business is registered for Value Added Tax.

The book-keeping is operated on a manual system, with a main ledger and subsidiary ledgers. The main ledger includes control accounts for sales ledger and purchases ledger (with customer and supplier accounts contained in subsidiary ledgers), and petty cash control account (with petty cash book forming the subsidiary ledger).

You have just started work as an accounts assistant and are responsible for all aspects of the book-keeping system. Your supervisor is Jane Jagpal, the office manager. A part-time accounts assistant, Mike Venn, helps you with the book-keeping.

TASKS

Today is 31 July 2004 and you only started working for 'Sunny Days' last week. There are a number of tasks that need to be completed today.

Task 1 A trial balance was not prepared at the end of last month, on 30 June 2004. A list of the balances of all the accounts at that date is given below. Transfer the balances to the relevant columns of the trial balance shown on page 315. Total the trial balance, and ensure that it balances by entering a suspense account balance.

Balances at 30 June 2004

	£
Purchases	227,435
Sales	362,024
Purchases returns	3,217
Sales returns	9,609
Discount allowed	1,482
Discount received	793
Wages	88,463
Rent paid	4,271
Rates	3,084
Bank charges	396
Postages	2,787
Stationery	1,824
Travel expenses	2,796
Bad debts written off	427

Sundry expenses	3,048
Vehicles	12,000
Office equipment	6,000
Stock	38,435
Petty cash control	100
Bank (debit balance)	11,900
Sales ledger control	102,371
Purchases ledger control	75,284
Value Added Tax (credit balance)	3,335
Loan from bank	15,000
Capital	75,000
Drawings	16,075
Suspense	?

Task 2 Enter the balances from the trial balance (Task 1) into the following accounts shown on pages 316 to 322:

Purchases
Sales
Purchases returns
Sales returns
Discount allowed
Discount received
Wages
Rent paid
Rates
Bank charges
Postages
Stationery
Travel expenses
Bad debts written off
Sundry expenses
Petty cash control
Sales ledger control
Purchases ledger control
Value Added Tax
Suspense

Notes:

- *enter the balances as 'balance b/d' using the date 1 July 2004*
- *other accounts from the trial balance, which are not listed above, are not required to be opened*

Task 3 The petty cash book for July has been written up by your assistant, Mike Venn, and is shown on page 323.

Total the columns and restore the imprest amount to £100 on 31 July 2004 – cash is to be withdrawn from the bank account using cheque number 101281, and the appropriate entry made in the cash book on page 327. Balance the petty cash book.

At 31 July 2004, after the petty cash has been restored to the imprest amount, a list of the notes and coins in the petty cash box at the close of business on 31 July 2004 is given on page 324, together with a reconciliation schedule. Complete the reconciliation schedule, including a note of any discrepancy.

Complete the double-entry transactions from petty cash book using the accounts shown on pages 316 to 322.

Task 4 The cash book for July 2004 has been written up during the month by your assistant, Mike Venn.

- Update the cash book on page 327 from the schedules of standing orders, direct debits and BACS receipts shown on page 325.
- Check the bank statement on page 326 against the cash book for accuracy, and update the cash book as necessary.
- Total the cash book, showing clearly the balance carried down.
- Prepare a bank reconciliation statement at 31 July 2004 which agrees the bank statement balance with the cash book balance (use page 327 for your answer).
- Complete double-entry from the cash book to the main ledger for the following accounts (shown on pages 316 to 322).

  Wages

  Rent paid

  Rates

  Bank charges

  Sales ledger control (see list of debtors below)

  Purchases ledger control (see list of creditors below)

To assist with this task, Mike Venn provides you with a list of the debtors and creditors of Sunny Days:

debtors	**creditors**
C & R Garden Centres	Alpha Manufacturing
Garden Time Limited	Dayton and Company
Osborne plc	Eveshore Woodwork
Raven Enterprises	RP Industries
Tyax Country Stores	Tritton Limited
Western DIY	Wyvern Wood
Woodland Garden Centre Limited	

Note: where appropriate, Mike Venn will make the entries in the subsidiary ledgers

Task 5 The office manager, Jane Jagpal, sends you the email (below).

- Prepare the journal entries referred to in the email, including appropriate narratives, using the journal page (on page 328).
- Record the journal entries in the double-entry accounts in the main ledger. (Note: Mike Venn will make any relevant entries in the subsidiary ledgers.)

EMAIL

from	Jane Jagpal
to	A Student
cc	
subject	Journal entries
date	31 July 2004

message

Hi

Please could you draw up two journal entries for me?

The first concerns our customer, Woodland Garden Centre Limited. They owe us £517.00, but have gone into liquidation so we have no chance of recovering the debt. Later on, we may be able to recover the VAT included in this amount but, for the moment, please write off the whole balance and ignore VAT.

The second concerns an error in our accounts of £50.00 of fuel for vehicles. The amount was debited in error to sundry expenses account, instead of to travel expenses account. Can you please make the correction?

Both of these matters should be dealt with by means of journals dated 31 July 2004.

Thanks

Jane

Task 6 Your assistant, Mike Venn, has kept the subsidiary (purchases) ledger up-to-date during the month. He provides you with the list of balances at 31 July 2004 shown on page 329. The totals of the purchases day book and purchases returns day book, and the total of discount received for the month are also shown on page 329.

- Record the double-entry from the day books and the discount total in the main ledger for the following accounts (shown on pages 316 to 322):

  Purchases

  Purchases returns

  Discount received

  Purchases ledger control

  Value Added Tax

- Total the purchases ledger control account at 31 July 2004, showing clearly the balance carried down (do not balance any other accounts at this stage).
- Reconcile the balance of the purchases ledger control account with the list of balances for the subsidiary (purchases) ledger. Use page 329 for your answer.
- In a note to Jane Jagpal, suggest a reason for any discrepancy you observe. Use page 331 for your answer.

Task 7 Your assistant, Mike Venn, has kept the subsidiary (sales) ledger up-to-date during the month. He provides you with the list of balances at 31 July 2004 shown on page 330. The totals of the sales day book and sales returns day book, and the total of discount allowed for the month are also shown on page 330.

- Record the double-entry from the day books and the discount total in the main (general) ledger for the following accounts (shown on pages 316 to 322):

  Sales

  Sales returns

  Discount allowed

  Sales ledger control

  Value Added Tax

- Total the sales ledger control account at 31 July 2004, showing clearly the balance carried down (do not balance any other accounts at this stage).
- Reconcile the balance of the sales ledger control account with the list of balances from the subsidiary (sales) ledger. Use page 330 for your answer.
- In a note to Jane Jagpal, suggest a reason for any discrepancy you observe. Use page 331 for your answer.

Task 8 The office manager, Jane Jagpal, sends you the email (below).

- Prepare the journal entries to correct the errors referred to in the email, including appropriate narratives. Use the journal page (on page 332).
- Record the journal entries in the double-entry accounts in the main ledger. Ensure that the balance of suspense account is cleared by these entries.

EMAIL

from	Jane Jagpal
to	A Student
cc	
subject	Correcting the trial balance
date	31 July 2004

message

Hi

I've looked into the discrepancy which showed up in last month's trial balance and I've found two items that have caused the problem.

The first is that a payment rent of £1,450 made on 17 June was correctly credited to bank account. However, no entry for this payment was recorded in rent paid account.

The second concerns the sales returns for June, amounting to £350. The figure was taken from the sales returns day book and entered correctly in sales ledger control account. However, in sales returns account, the figure was mistakenly entered as a credit. I've checked and can confirm that the returns items have been correctly recorded in the subsidiary (sales) ledger.

Both of these matters should be dealt with by means of journals dated 31 July 2004.

Thanks

Jane

Task 9

- Balance all the main ledger accounts shown on pages 316 to 322 at 31 July 2004, showing clearly the balance carried down.
- Transfer the balances to the trial balance on page 333.
- Transfer the balance of bank account (page 327) to the trial balance on page 333.
- Transfer from the trial balance at 30 June 2004 (page 315) to the trial balance at 31 July 2004 the balances of the following accounts:

  Vehicles

  Office equipment

  Stock

  Loan from bank

  Capital

  Drawings

- Total each column of the trial balance: the debit column and credit column should be the same.

Task 10 As you have recently joined Sunny Days the office manager, Jane Jagpal, asks for your views on aspects of the accounts system and the way the accounts office is run. In particular, she mentions the following:

- With only yourself (full-time) and Mike Venn (part-time) as accounts staff, the accounts office is often empty at various times of the day, eg lunch time, and at morning and afternoon breaks.
- The computer used for payroll is often left switched on all day.
- The petty cash box is kept on top of a desk with the key either in the box or hanging from a hook close by.
- Double-entry accounting records are kept out on the desk all the time.
- Trial balances are kept in the filing cabinet, but the key to the cabinet has been lost and the drawers are kept unlocked.

Write a note to Jane Jagpal highlighting the problems and suggesting improvements.

Use page 334 for your answer.

ANSWER PAGES

Task 1

TRIAL BALANCE OF SUNNY DAYS AS AT 30 JUNE 2004

	Debit	*Credit*
	£	£
Name of account		
Purchases	....	....
Sales	....	....
Purchases returns	....	....
Sales returns	....	....
Discount allowed	....	....
Discount received	....	....
Wages	....	....
Rent paid	....	....
Rates	....	....
Bank charges	....	....
Postages	....	....
Stationery	....	....
Travel expenses	....	....
Bad debts written off	....	....
Sundry expenses	....	....
Vehicles	....	....
Office equipment	....	....
Stock	....	....
Petty cash control	....	....
Bank	....	....
Sales ledger control	....	....
Purchases ledger control	....	....
Value Added Tax	....	....
Loan from bank	....	....
Capital	....	....
Drawings	....	....
Suspense	....	....
TOTAL	....	....

Tasks 2 – 8

Note: The lines shown in the accounts are there to help you present your work neatly and clearly. You may not need to use all of the lines.

MAIN LEDGER

Purchases

Date	*Details*	*Amount* £	*Date*	*Details*	*Amount* £

Sales

Date	*Details*	*Amount* £	*Date*	*Details*	*Amount* £

Tasks 2 – 8 continued

MAIN LEDGER

Purchases Returns

Date	*Details*	*Amount* £	*Date*	*Details*	*Amount* £

Sales Returns

Date	*Details*	*Amount* £	*Date*	*Details*	*Amount* £

Discount Allowed

Date	*Details*	*Amount* £	*Date*	*Details*	*Amount* £

Tasks 2 – 8 continued

MAIN LEDGER

Discount Received

Date	Details	Amount £	Date	Details	Amount £

Wages

Date	Details	Amount £	Date	Details	Amount £

Rent Paid

Date	Details	Amount £	Date	Details	Amount £

Tasks 2 – 8 continued

MAIN LEDGER

Rates

Date	Details	Amount £	Date	Details	Amount £

Bank Charges

Date	Details	Amount £	Date	Details	Amount £

Postages

Date	Details	Amount £	Date	Details	Amount £

Tasks 2 – 8 continued

MAIN LEDGER

Stationery

Date	*Details*	*Amount* £	*Date*	*Details*	*Amount* £

Travel Expenses

Date	*Details*	*Amount* £	*Date*	*Details*	*Amount* £

Bad Debts Written Off

Date	*Details*	*Amount* £	*Date*	*Details*	*Amount* £

Tasks 2 – 8 continued

MAIN LEDGER

Sundry Expenses

Date	*Details*	*Amount* £	*Date*	*Details*	*Amount* £

Petty Cash Control

Date	*Details*	*Amount* £	*Date*	*Details*	*Amount* £

Sales Ledger Control

Date	*Details*	*Amount* £	*Date*	*Details*	*Amount* £

Tasks 2 – 8 continued

MAIN LEDGER

Purchases Ledger Control

Date	*Details*	*Amount* £	*Date*	*Details*	*Amount* £

Value Added Tax

Date	*Details*	*Amount* £	*Date*	*Details*	*Amount* £

Suspense

Date	*Details*	*Amount* £	*Date*	*Details*	*Amount* £

Task 3

Petty Cash Book									PCB 47
Receipts	Date	Details	Voucher No	Total Payment	Analysis columns				
					VAT	Postages	Stationery	Travel	Sundry
£	2004			£	£	£	£	£	£
100.00	1 Jul	Balance b/d							
	5 Jul	Taxi fare	78	5.46	0.81			4.65	
	9 Jul	Stationery	79	9.40	1.40		8.00		
	12 Jul	Postages	80	4.30		4.30			
	17 Jul	Donation	81	5.00					5.00
	20 Jul	Rail fare	82	8.09				8.09	
	24 Jul	Stationery	83	7.05	1.05		6.00		
	27 Jul	Postages	84	6.70		6.70			
	31 Jul	Taxi fare	85	5.00	0.74			4.26	

Task 3 continued

Notes and coin in the petty cash tin, 31 July 2004

Value	Number	Total value £
£20	2	
£10	2	
£5	4	
£1	8	
50p	17	
20p	8	
10p	12	
5p	8	
2p	9	
1p	12	

Petty cash reconciliation

Date: ______________________

	£
Balance per petty cash book	....
Total of notes and coin	....
Discrepancy (if any)	....

Explanation of discrepancy (if any)

....

....

....

Task 4

SCHEDULE OF STANDING ORDERS AND DIRECT DEBITS

Date due	Details of recipient	Amount	Authorised by
5th each month, from August 2004 to July 2007	Wyvern National Bank – loan account repayments	£625	Jane Jagpal
17th each month, from January 2004 until further notice	Astra Property Rental – rent paid on business premises	£1,450	Jane Jagpal
18th each month, from April 2004 to March 2005 inclusive	Wyvern Council – rates	£696	Jane Jagpal

SCHEDULE OF BACS RECEIPTS

Date due	Details of sender	Amount
20th each month, from April 2004 until further notice	Tyax Country Stores – debtor	£2,000
28th each month, from September 2004 until further notice	Garden Time Limited – debtor	£1,500

Task 4 continued

WYVERN NATIONAL BANK PLC

PO Box 301, Broad Street, Wyvern WY1 2DB

Account: Sunny Days Garden Products **Statement no:** 432

Account no: 80423621

Date: 31 July 2004

STATEMENT OF ACCOUNT

Date	Details	Payments	Receipts	Balance
2004		£	£	£
1 Jul	Balance b/d			14,976
3 Jul	Credit		12,747	27,723
5 Jul	Credit		8,932	36,655
9 Jul	Cheque No 101274	10,854		25,801
11 Jul	Credit		15,073	40,874
16 Jul	Cheque No 101276	10,347		30,527
16 Jul	Cheque No 101275	3,076		27,451
17 Jul	DD: Astra Property Rental	1,450		26,001
18 Jul	Credit		3,096	29,097
19 Jul	BACS: Tyax Country Stores		2,000	31,097
20 Jul	SO: Wyvern Council	696		30,401
23 Jul	Cheque No 101277	4,863		25,538
27 Jul	Cheque No 101278	6,405		19,133
31 Jul	Cheque No 101280	11,292		7,841
31 Jul	Bank charges	55		7,786

BACS Automated transfer SO Standing Order DD Direct Debit

Task 4 continued

CASH BOOK

Date	Details	Bank	Date	Details	Cheque number	Bank
2004		£	2004			£
1 Jul	Balance b/d	11,900	2 Jul	RP Industries	101274	10,854
3 Jul	Western DIY	12,747	6 Jul	Wages	101275	3,076
5 Jul	Raven Enterprises	8,932	10 Jul	Alpha Manufacturing	101276	10,347
11 Jul	Western DIY	15,073	16 Jul	Wyvern Wood	101277	4,863
18 Jul	Garden Time Ltd	3,096	20 Jul	Tritton Ltd	101278	6,405
31 Jul	Osborne plc	2,854	27 Jul	Dayton & Co	101279	2,741
			31 Jul	Wages	101280	11,292

SUNNY DAYS GARDEN PRODUCTS

Bank Reconciliation Statement as at 31 July 2004

Task 5

JOURNAL

Date	Details	Debit	Credit
		£	£

Task 6

Details for reconciliation of the purchases ledger control account

Purchases day book:

	Total	VAT	Net
Totals for July 2004	£58,280	£8,680	£49,600

Purchases returns day book:

	Total	VAT	Net
Totals for July 2004	£2,068	£308	£1,760

Discount received: total for month £307

Balances in subsidiary (purchases) ledger at 31 July 2004	£
Alpha Manufacturing	19,498
Dayton and Company	17,304
Eveshore Woodwork	8,794
RP Industries	22,153
Tritton Limited	18,743
Wyvern Wood	9,487

Reconciliation of purchases ledger control account at 31 July 2004

	£	£
Closing balance of purchases ledger control account		....
Balances of accounts in subsidiary (purchases) ledger:		
Alpha Manufacturing	....	
Dayton and Company	....	
Eveshore Woodwork	....	
RP Industries	....	
Tritton Limited	....	
Wyvern Wood	....	
Total		....
Discrepancy (if any)		....

Task 7

Details for reconciliation of the sales ledger control account

Sales day book:

	Total	VAT	Net
Totals for July 2004	£73,320	£10,920	£62,400

Sales returns day book:

	Total	VAT	Net
Totals for July 2004	£2,632	£392	£2,240

Discount allowed: total for month £478

Balances in subsidiary (sales) ledger at 31 July 2004	£
C & R Garden Centres	35,090
Garden Time Limited	16,816
Osborne plc	12,893
Raven Enterprises	11,204
Tyax Country Stores	8,974
Western DIY	42,376

Reconciliation of sales ledger control account at 31 July 2004

	£	£
Closing balance of sales ledger control account		....
Balances of accounts in subsidiary (sales) ledger:		
C & R Garden Centres	....	
Garden Time Limited	....	
Osborne plc	....	
Raven Enterprises	....	
Tyax Country Stores	....	
Western DIY	....	
Total		....
Discrepancy (if any)		....

Tasks 6 and 7

Note to Jane Jagpal, Office Manager

Task 8

JOURNAL

Date	Details	Debit	Credit
		£	£

Task 9

TRIAL BALANCE OF SUNNY DAYS AS AT 31 JULY 2004

Name of account	*Debit* £	*Credit* £
Purchases	....	....
Sales	....	....
Purchases returns	....	....
Sales returns	....	....
Discount allowed	....	....
Discount received	....	....
Wages	....	....
Rent paid	....	....
Rates	....	....
Bank charges	....	....
Postages	....	....
Stationery	....	....
Travel expenses	....	....
Bad debts written off	....	....
Sundry expenses	....	....
Vehicles	....	....
Office equipment	....	....
Stock	....	....
Petty cash control	....	....
Bank	....	....
Sales ledger control	....	....
Purchases ledger control	....	....
Value Added Tax	....	....
Loan from bank	....	....
Capital	....	....
Drawings	....	....
Suspense	....	....
TOTAL	....	....

Task 10

Note to Jane Jagpal, Office Manager

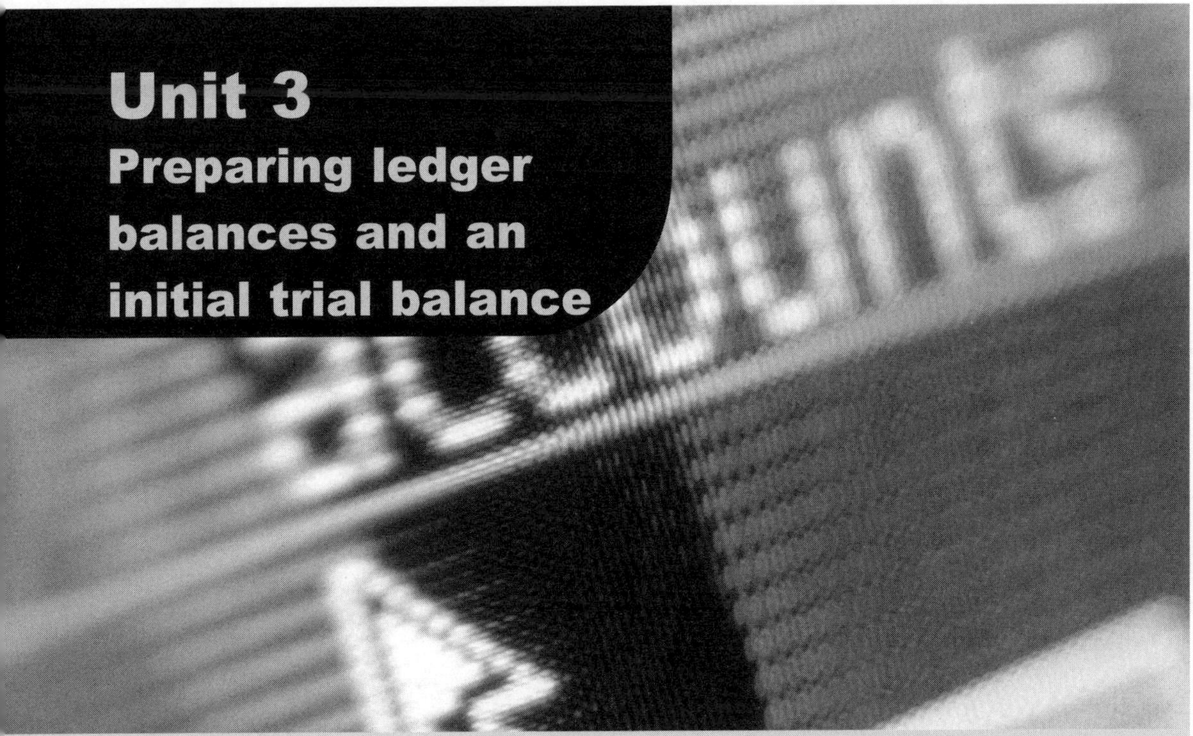

Unit 3
Preparing ledger balances and an initial trial balance

Simulation 6: Weasley Supplies

(adapted from AAT sample material)

NVQ Element coverage

3.1 bank balance transactions

3.2 prepare ledger balances and control accounts

3.3 draft an initial trial balance

Scenario and contents

This Simulation is based on Weasley Supplies.

The tasks in the Simulation include:

- checking the bank statement against the cash book for accuracy, updating the cash book as necessary, and preparing a bank reconciliation statement
- journal entries, including the correction of errors
- restoring the imprest amount of petty cash book, balancing the account, and reconciling the cash held
- the operation of sales ledger and purchases ledger control accounts, including reconciliation of subsidiary ledgers
- preparation of a trial balance

Suggested time allocation: three hours plus 15 minutes reading time

SIMULATION 6
WEASLEY SUPPLIES

SITUATION

Your name is Kim Wendell. You are a qualified accounting technician working for Weasley Supplies. You report to the manager, Ari Pottle.

All of the company's sales and purchases are on credit terms.

The books of account are maintained in manual form.

Today's date is Monday 7 July 2004, and you will be dealing with transactions taking place in June 2004.

Ledgers

A sales ledger control account and a purchases ledger control account are maintained in the main (general) ledger. There is a subsidiary (sales) ledger for customers and a subsidiary (purchases) ledger for suppliers.

Bank account and cash book

A bank statement is received monthly. Entries on the bank statement are compared with:

- entries in the cash book:
- a schedule of standing orders, direct debits and credit transfers.

The cash book is updated as appropriate in the light of the bank statement and the schedule of standing orders, direct debits and credit transfers. The main items paid for by standing order, direct debit and credit transfer are:

- business rates;
- insurance and leasing payments;
- staff salaries;
- the company's credit card bill.

These items are analysed as 'Other payments' in the cash book.

TASKS

Task 1

Refer to the schedule of standing orders, direct debits and credit transfers on page 338, and the bank statement for June 2004 on page 339.

- Enter the appropriate details from the schedule in the cash book for June 2004 on page 343.
- Also enter any other items on the bank statement not so far recorded in the cash book.

Note: You must complete both the total columns and the analysis columns in the cash book.

Task 2

Total all columns of the cash book and bring down a balance as at close of business on 30 June 2004.

Task 3

Prepare a bank reconciliation statement as at 30 June 2004, clearly identifying all discrepancies between the cash book and the bank statement. Use blank page 344.

Task 4

Refer to the email from Ari Pottle on page 340.

- Prepare the journals referred to in the email, including appropriate narrative, using the journal vouchers on page 345.

Task 5

- Post from the cash book (Task 2) and the journals (Task 4) to the sales ledger control account and the purchases ledger control account on page 346. (You are not required to make entries in the subsidiary ledgers in respect of these journals.)
- Total the two control accounts and bring down balances as at close of business on 30 June 2004.

Task 6

Refer to the list of balances on page 341, which have been taken from the subsidiary (purchases) ledger on 30 June 2004.

- Total the list of balances and reconcile the total with the balance on the purchases ledger control account.
- Suggest a reason for any discrepancy you observe.

Present your work on blank page 347.

Task 7

The petty cash book has been written up for the month of June 2004 – see page 348. On page 349 you will see a list of the notes and coins in the petty cash tin at close of business on 30 June 2004, and a reconciliation schedule.

- Total the petty cash book and bring down a balance at close of business on 30 June 2004.
- Complete the reconciliation schedule, including a note of any discrepancy.

Task 8

Refer to the list of ledger balances prepared by Ari Pottle as at 30 June 2004 (page 341).

- Enter Ari's balances, and also the control account balances computed in Tasks 2, 5 and 7, onto the trial balance on page 350. Note that the balance to be entered for cash at bank should reflect the journal entries drafted in Task 4.
- Total the trial balance, and ensure that it balances by entering a suspense account balance.

Task 9

After informing Ari Pottle of the suspense account balance, you have now received the email on page 342.

- Prepare the journals referred to in the email, including appropriate narrative, using the journal vouchers on page 351.

Task 10

Enter the journals prepared in Task 9 into the suspense account on page 351 and ensure that the closing balance on this account is zero.

Task 11

Reply to Ari's email explaining how the journals prepared in Task 9 will affect the trial balance and confirming that it will now balance. Use the blank email form on page 352.

Schedule of standing orders, direct debits and credit transfers (extract)

Standing orders	**Amount**	**When payable**
Standing orders		
Medwith Borough Council (business rates)	£600	Monthly from April to January inclusive; no payment in February, March
Safeguard Insurance	£310	Monthly
Finance Leasing plc	£425	March, June, September, December
Direct debits		
Purchasecard plc	Variable	Monthly
Credit transfers		
Staff salaries	Variable	Monthly

Northern Bank plc **STATEMENT**

27 High Street, Malliton FR5 6EW 27-76-54

Account: Weasley Supplies Statement No: 226

Account Number: 22314561

Date	Details		Payments	Receipts	Balance
			£	£	£
2004					
1 June	Balance from previous sheet				5,267.88
6 June	Cash/cheques received	CC		4,776.15	10,044.03
10 June	Cheque 331174		781.03		9,263.00
13 June	Cheque 331175		1,456.91		
13 June	Cash/cheques received	CC		7,715.96	15,522.05
17 June	Safeguard Insurance 30056561	SO	310.00		15,212.05
20 June	Cash/cheques received	CC		15,901.22	31,113.27
23 June	Medwith BC 4412341125	SO	600.00		30,513.27
24 June	Cheque 331176		9,912.75		
24 June	Cash/cheques received	CC		2,816.55	23,417.07
25 June	Cheque 331177		3,901.25		19,515.82
26 June	Bank interest and charges	CHGS	107.33		
26 June	Finance Leasing plc 771233115	SO	425.00		
26 June	Salaries	CT	8,215.50		10,767.99
27 June	Purchasecard plc	DD	2,341.89		8,426.10
30 June	Cash/cheques received	CC		2,451.88	
30 June	Cheque 331179		3,126.99		7,750.99

Key SO Standing Order CC Cash and/or cheques CT Credit transfer
O/D Overdrawn D/D Direct Debit CHGS Bank charges

EMAIL

from	Ari Pottle
to	Kim Wendell
cc	
subject	Journal entries
date	7 July 2004

message

Hi Kim

Please could you draw up two journal entries for me please?

The first concerns our cheque number 331179. This has been logged in the cash book at an amount of £3,216.99, but in fact was for £3,126.99. The wrong amount has also been posted to the purchases ledger control account.

The second concerns our customer Driftway Limited. They owe us £1,233.75, but have gone into liquidation so we have no chance of recovering the debt. Later on we may be able to recover the VAT included in this amount, but for the moment please write off the whole balance and ignore VAT.

Both of these matters should be dealt with by means of journals dated 30 June 2004.

Thanks

Ari

Creditors' balances at 30 June 2004

	£
Earley and Partners	3,990.65
Horsfall Limited	2,561.22
James Ross	4,016.73
Peters Limited	2,351.67
Pickard Newton (debit balance)	(90.00)
Stainton and Co	3,109.81
Other creditors	5,667.54

Main (general) ledger: balances at 30 June 2004

	£
Administration expenses	3,276.88
Bad debts	2,010.76
Bank	Own figure
Business rates	1,800.00
Capital	46,745.76
Fixed assets	25,219.05
Inland Revenue	4,003.51
Insurance	930.00
Leasing costs	1,275.00
Petty cash	Own figure
Purchases	64,016.83
Purchases ledger control	Own figure
Purchases returns	1,125.31
Salaries expense	35,211.81
Sales	96,558.43
Sales and distribution expenses	2,006.81
Sales ledger control	Own figure
Sales returns	1,327.44
Stock	7,270.00
VAT control (credit balance)	3,995.20

EMAIL

from	Ari Pottle
to	Kim Wendell
cc	
subject	Correcting the trial balance
date	7 July 2004

message

Hi Kim

I've looked into the discrepancy on the initial trial balance, and I've found two items that cause the problem.

First, we returned goods to a supplier to the value of £200. We correctly entered this in the subsidiary (purchases) ledger, and in the purchases ledger control account. However, in the purchases returns account we mistakenly entered it as a debit.

Second, we received a cheque for £3,000 which was correctly debited to bank account. However, no credit entry was made. The double entry should have been completed in the capital account.

Please could you draft journals dated 30 June 2004 to deal with both of these items, and then let me have a reply to this message confirming that the trial balance will now balance.

Thanks

Ari

ANSWER PAGES

Tasks 1 and 2

RECEIPTS								CB 241 PAYMENTS
Sales ledger £	**Other receipts £**	**Total £**	**Date 2004**	**Details**	**Cheque number**	**Total £**	**Purchases ledger £**	**Other payments £**
		4,486.85	1 Jun	Balance b/f				
4,776.15		4,776.15	5 Jun	Metrix plc				
			6 Jun	Horsfall Limited	331175	1,456.91	1,456.91	
7,715.96		7,715.96	12 Jun	Plympton Limited				
			16 Jun	Stainton and Co	331176	9,912.75	9,912.75	
			16 Jun	Inland Revenue	331177	3,901.25		3,901.25
15,901.22		15,901.22	19 Jun	Maidstone plc				
			23 Jun	Earley and Partners	331178	3,341.20	3,341.20	
2,816.55		2,816.55	23 Jun	Stenshaw Limited				
			25 Jun	Pickard Newton	331179	3,216.99	3,216.99	
2,451.88		2,451.88	29 Jun	Fitzroy Limited				
1,926.34		1,926.34	30 Jun	Dove Ambleside				

Task 3

Task 4

JOURNAL

Date	*Account names and narrative*	*Debit*	*Credit*
2004		£	£

Task 5

MAIN (GENERAL) LEDGER

Account Sales ledger control account

Debit					Credit
Date 2004	Details	Amount £	Date 2004	Details	Amount £
1 Jun	Balance b/f	30,914.66			
30 Jun	Invoices in month	32,617.80			

Account Purchases ledger control account

Debit					Credit
Date 2004	Details	Amount £	Date 2004	Details	Amount £
			1 Jun	Balance b/f	19,334.02
			30 Jun	Invoices in month	20,201.45

Task 6

Task 7

Petty Cash Book **PCB 52**

Receipts £	Date 2004	Details	Voucher number	Total £	VAT £	Postage £	Stationery £	Other expenses £
200.00	1 Jun	Balance b/f						
	5 Jun	Postage	358	4.26		4.26		
	9 Jun	Stationery	359	12.87	1.91		10.96	
	12 Jun	Tea, coffee, etc	360	7.02				7.02
	16 Jun	Postage	361	3.12		3.12		
	18 Jun	Stationery	362	13.51	2.01		11.50	
	23 Jun	Stationery	363	6.58	0.98		5.60	
	26 Jun	Stationery	364	5.73	0.85		4.88	
	27 Jun	Postage	365	5.90		5.90		
	30 Jun	Tea, coffee, etc	366	6.50				6.50

Task 7 continued

Notes and coin in the petty cash tin, 30 June 2004

Value	Number	Total value
		£
£20	4	
£10	3	
£5	2	
£1	8	
50p	8	
20p	8	
10p	8	
5p	1	
2p	2	
1p	2	

Petty cash reconciliation

Date: ______________________

	£
Balance per petty cash book	....
Total of notes and coin	....
Discrepancy (if any)	....

Explanation of discrepancy (if any)

....

....

....

Task 8

Trial balance at 30 June 2004

	Ledger balances	
Account	**Debit** £	**Credit** £
Administration expenses		
Bad debts		
Bank		
Business rates		
Capital		
Fixed assets		
Inland Revenue		
Insurance		
Leasing costs		
Petty cash		
Purchases		
Purchases ledger control		
Purchases returns		
Salaries expense		
Sales		
Sales and distribution expenses		
Sales ledger control		
Sales returns		
Stock		
VAT control		
Suspense		
Totals		

Tasks 9 and 10

JOURNAL

Date 2004	*Account names and narrative*	*Debit* £	*Credit* £

Account Suspense

Debit					Credit
Date 2004	Details	Amount £	Date 2004	Details	Amount £

Task 11

EMAIL

from	Kim Wendell
to	Ari Pottle
cc	
subject	Correcting the trial balance
date	7 July 2004

message

. . . .

. . . .

. . . .

. . . .

. . . .

. . . .

. . . .

. . . .

. . . .

. . . .

. . . .

. . . .

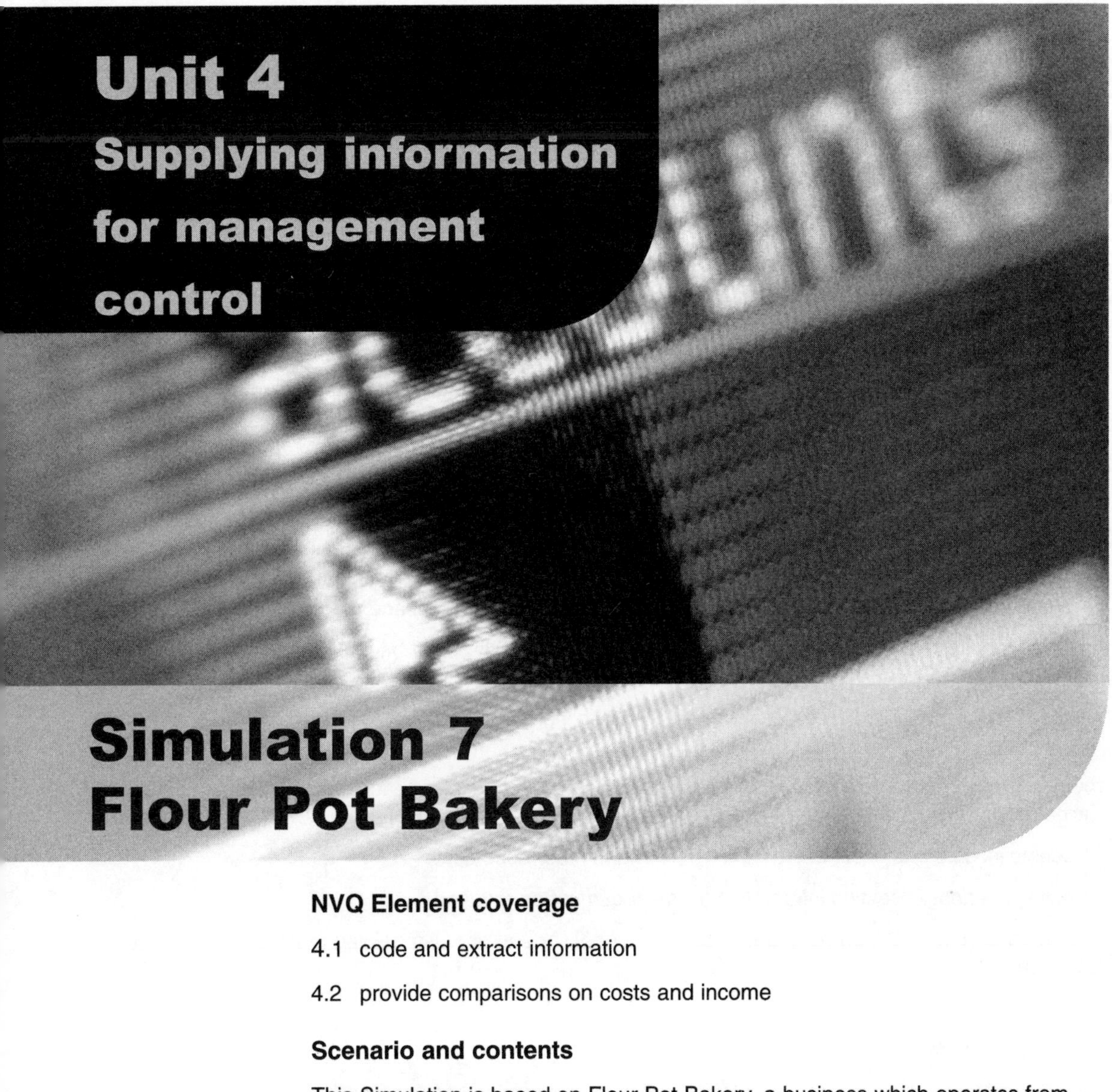

Unit 4
Supplying information for management control

Simulation 7
Flour Pot Bakery

NVQ Element coverage

4.1 code and extract information

4.2 provide comparisons on costs and income

Scenario and contents

This Simulation is based on Flour Pot Bakery, a business which operates from four shops in the Wyvern area and produces bread, pastries, speciality cakes and 'take-away' snacks. The tasks in the simulation involve providing financial information and reports to management. They include:

- the coding of sales figures, suppliers' invoices and payroll data
- checking coding on invoices and identifying errors
- completing a performance report for cost centres and identifying discrepancies
- completing a performance report for sales and identifying discrepancies
- dealing with queries which involve confidentiality and referral

Suggested time allocation: three hours plus fifteen minutes reading time

SIMULATION 7
FLOUR POT BAKERY

SITUATION

You are Alex Wright, an Accounts Assistant at the main office of Flour Pot Bakery Limited, at 61 Fore Street, Wyvern WV1 3GH. The company is VAT registered.

The business operates at four locations:

- the main office and production facility at Wyvern – these premises also include a shop counter
- three shops in the nearby towns of Appleford, Great Marcle and Norton

Flour Pot Bakery has three types of product, all of which are produced at Wyvern:

- bread and 'everyday' cakes such as doughnuts, rock cakes, pastries and cream cakes
- 'take-away' film-wrapped and packaged rolls, sandwiches and filled baguettes, mainly for lunchtime customers
- speciality personalised iced cakes made to order, eg wedding cakes, birthday cakes, anniversary cakes

Your work as an Accounts Assistant involves supplying accounting information for the management of the business. This includes:

- coding income and expenditure from invoices and other documents
- extracting and presenting information for management as required

You report directly to Mike Moore, the Accounts Supervisor and are also helping to train a new assistant, Jade Simmons.

CODING SYSTEM

The six digit coding system used by Flour Pot Bakery is organised as follows:

coding of income

Example: 10 30 05

The first two digits are always 10, which shows that it is an *income item* (the code for costs is 20)

The second two digits show the *profit centre*:

10	Appleford
20	Great Marcle
30	Norton
40	Wyvern

The final two digits show the *type of product* which was sold:

05	bread and cakes
15	packaged 'take-away' snacks
25	speciality 'to order' cakes

coding of costs

Example: 20 30 05

The first two digits are always 20, which shows that it is an *cost item* (the code for income is 10)

The second two digits show the *cost centre* (which is always allocated to the Wyvern site):

50	baking
60	cake icing for speciality cakes
70	packaging
80	administration/shop costs
90	advertising

The final two digits show the *classification of cost:*

55	materials
65	labour
75	expenses

Examples of the coding system in use

Norton shop sales of bread	103005	=	income (10) from Norton (30) from bread and cakes (05)
Wyvern shop sale of sandwiches	104015	=	income (10) from Wyvern (40) from sandwiches (15)
Wages paid to bakery workers	205065	=	a cost (20) from baking (30) related to labour (65)
Film used to wrap sandwiches	207055	=	a cost (20) from packaging (70) materials (55)

TASKS

1 The date is 31 May 2004. You have in front of you the Daily Coding Sheet (page 357) which shows the income and expenditure against each code for the month to date.

There are a number of purchases invoices in your in-tray (pages 358 to 360) that need to be coded. For each of these you work out the appropriate code and write the number in the coding 'box' on the invoice. Mike Moore, the Accounts Supervisor, reminds you that the costs of the photocopier are to be shared equally between the administration and advertising departments.

After coding, you enter the money amounts of the invoices on the Daily Coding Sheet in the column for 31 May. Note that amounts are to be rounded to the nearest £; any VAT element of invoices is to be ignored – this is coded separately.

2 Towards the end of the day, on 31 May, the four shop managers e-mail (page 361) you with details of their sales (excluding any VAT element) for the day. You code this income and enter it on the Daily Coding Sheet (page 357). Remember to round amounts to the nearest £.

3 On 31 May the Staff Manager gives you payroll details for the week commencing 21 May of two employees who have recently joined the company. They are:

Ramjit Singh (baking department) – worked 40 hours on basic pay of £5 per hour, plus 4 hours of overtime at £7.50 per hour. There was no bonus or commission and the employer's National Insurance Contributions amounted to £17.81.

Daisy Chang (administration department) – worked 40 hours on basic pay of £5.50 per hour, but no overtime. There was no bonus or commission and the employer's National Insurance Contributions amounted to £16.59.

You are to enter these details on the schedules on page 362 to work out the labour cost to the business.

You are then to update the Daily Coding Sheet (page 357) with this data as it has not yet been entered. Remember to round amounts to the nearest £.

Note that the company's policy is to charge all payroll costs (including overtime and employer's National Insurance Contributions) to labour costs.

4 From the Daily Coding Sheet (page 357) you calculate the new balances for the month to date at the end of 31 May. These month-end figures are then taken to the summary of income and expenditure (page 363) and listed in the current month column.

On the summary of income and expenditure you complete the column for the year to 31 May 2004.

5 From the calculations performed in Task 4 you are to complete the Cost Performance Report for materials, labour and expenses on page 364.

6 Mike Moore, the Accounts Supervisor has asked you to examine the figures on the Cost Performance Report for materials, labour and expenses on page 364 and to calculate the cost differences (variances) on the Report form on page 364. You are to identify any differences (variances) of 10% or more and note them on the bottom of the form.

7 From the calculations performed in Task 4 you are to complete the Sales Performance Report for sales for the four shops on page 365.

8 Mike Moore, the Accounts Supervisor has also asked you to examine the figures on the Sales Performance Report for sales on page 365 and to calculate the differences (variances) on the report form on page 365. You are again to identify any differences (variances) of 10% or more and note them on the bottom of the form.

9 The date is 1 June 2004. You have been asked to check the coding on three supplier invoices received in the post today and processed by the trainee Jade Simmons (pages 366 to 367). Write down on the note (page 367) any errors you think you need to bring to her attention.

10 The date is 1 June 2004. While you are at lunch Jade takes a message (page 368) from the manager of the Norton shop who is asking for the sales figures for all the shops. The figures have been requested by a market research company. Write down (page 368) what you think you would tell Jade about the release of this information and the authorisation needed.

DAILY CODING SHEET: INCOME AND EXPENDITURE **Date:** 31 May 2004

MONTH TO: 30 MAY 2004

Note: figures are rounded to nearest £

Code No	Month to date (£)	Amounts for 31 May (£)	Month to date: new balance (£)
101005	25,076		
101015	30,164		
101025	4,024		
102005	15,958		
102015	10,844		
102025	4,091		
103005	22,032		
103015	13,197		
103025	6,478		
104005	31,070		
104015	35,264		
104025	17,406		
205055	51,287		
205065	42,753		
205075	20,264		
206055	6,833		
206065	9,170		
206075	6,182		
207055	5,437		
207065	10,551		
207075	8,327		
208055	3,596		
208065	12,504		
208075	6,652		
209055	4,076		
209065	10,387		
209075	3,932		

INVOICE

WYVERN MILLERS LIMITED

The Mill, Wyvern, WV4 1QT
VAT Reg 341 7821 27

CODE:

invoice to

Flour Pot Bakery Limited
61 Fore Street
Wyvern
WV1 3GH

invoice no	**6281**
account	**3191**
your reference	**367**
date/tax point	**25 May 2004**

product code	description	quantity	price	unit	total	discount	net
351	Stoneground baking flour	50	18.50	bag	925.00	0.00	925.00

goods total	925.00
VAT	0.00
TOTAL	925.00

terms
Net 30 days

INVOICE

Bakers Supplies Limited

47 Smith Street, London, EC3V 9AQ
VAT Reg 472 8391 82

CODE:

invoice to

Flour Pot Bakery Limited
61 Fore Street
Wyvern
WV1 3GH

invoice no	**3741**
account	**2741**
your reference	**369**
date/tax point	**25 05 04**

product code	description	quantity	price	unit	total	discount	net
861	Cake boxes, size 5	500	0.25	each	125.00	0.00	125.00

goods total	125.00
VAT	21.87
TOTAL	146.87

terms
Net 30 days

INVOICE
Wyvern Engineering Company

CODE:

Brunel Road, Wyvern, WV3 8TA
VAT Reg 278 3524 91

invoice to

Flour Pot Bakery Limited
61 Fore Street
Wyvern
WV1 3GH

invoice no 4071
account 0308
your reference 361
date/tax point 24 05 04

product code	description	quantity	price	unit	total	discount	net
001	Repairs to cake icing machine	1	155.00	each	155.00	0.00	155.00

goods total	155.00
VAT	27.12
TOTAL	182.12

terms
Net 30 days

CODE:

INVOICE
Severnvale Photocopiers Limited

Unit 40, Severn Business Park, Bridgetown, BG2 8QP
VAT Reg 396 0451 76

invoice to

Flour Pot Bakery Limited
61 Fore Street
Wyvern
WV1 3GH

invoice no 7046
account 0989
your reference 375
date/tax point 29 May 2004

product code	description	quantity	price	unit	total	discount	net
105	Service charge on Torriba photocopier	1	89.50	each	89.50	0.00	89.50

goods total	89.50
VAT	15.66
TOTAL	105.16

terms
Net 30 days

INVOICE

CODE:

Jarvis Advertising Services

48 East Street, Hollycombe, TU26 8LV
VAT Reg 981 3976 42

invoice to

Flour Pot Bakery Limited
61 Fore Street
Wyvern
WV1 3GH

invoice no	7842
account	0519
your reference	305
date/tax point	25 05 04

product code	description	quantity	price	unit	total	discount	net
HSB	Summer advertising promotion	1	785.00	each	785.00	0.00	785.00

goods total	785.00
VAT	137.37
TOTAL	922.37

terms
Net 30 days

INVOICE

Osborne Stationery Limited

Unit 5, Temeside Estate, Clifton Wells, CL4 7AP
VAT Reg 334 7921 45

CODE:

invoice to

Flour Pot Bakery Limited
61 Fore Street
Wyvern
WV1 3GH

invoice no	2073
account	3743
your reference	371
date/tax point	29 May 2004

product code	description	quantity	price	unit	total	discount	net
HT45	Box files, black	50	2.50	each	125.00	00.00	125.00

goods total	125.00
VAT	21.87
TOTAL	146.87

terms
Net 30 days

TEXT OF E-MAILS RECEIVED FROM THE FOUR SHOPS

To: Alex Wright, Accounts Assistant
From: Manager, Appleford
Date: 31 May 2004
Sales report: Appleford shop

Bread and cakes	£974.54
Packaged 'take-away' snacks	£1,386.68
Speciality cakes	£251.22

All figures are net of VAT, where appropriate.

To: Alex Wright, Accounts Assistant
From: Manager, Great Marcle
Date: 31 May 2004
Sales report: Great Marcle shop

Bread and cakes	£732.36
Packaged 'take-away' snacks	£401.49
Speciality cakes	£198.89

All figures are net of VAT, where appropriate.

To: Alex Wright, Accounts Assistant
From: Manager, Norton
Date: 31 May 2004
Sales report: Norton shop

Bread and cakes	£842.08
Packaged 'take-away' snacks	£508.76
Speciality cakes	£312.94

All figures are net of VAT, where appropriate.

To: Alex Wright, Accounts Assistant
From: Manager, Wyvern
Date: 31 May 2004
Sales report: Wyvern shop

Bread and cakes	£1,245.33
Packaged 'take-away' snacks	£1,348.60
Speciality cakes	£797.27

All figures are net of VAT, where appropriate.

PAYROLL COSTING SCHEDULE		
Name	Payroll period	
Department		TOTAL (£)
Basic pay hours	Pay rate (per hour)	
Overtime hours	Pay rate (per hour)	
Bonus		
Commission		
Employer's NICs		
	TOTAL EMPLOYER COST	
	CODE	
	input by	date

PAYROLL COSTING SCHEDULE		
Name	Payroll period	
Department		TOTAL (£)
Basic pay hours	Pay rate (per hour)	
Overtime hours	Pay rate (per hour)	
Bonus		
Commission		
Employer's NICs		
	TOTAL EMPLOYER COST	
	CODE	
	input by	date

SUMMARY: INCOME AND EXPENDITURE
YEAR ENDING 31 DECEMBER 2004

Code No	Description	Year to 30 Apr 2004 (£)	Current month: May 2004 (£)	Year to 31 May 2004 (£)
	INCOME			
	Bread and cakes			
101005	Appleford	123,049		
102005	Great Marcle	90,078		
103005	Norton	102,076		
104005	Wyvern	152,731		
	Packaged snacks			
101015	Appleford	161,421		
102015	Great Marcle	47,385		
103015	Norton	60,996		
104015	Wyvern	167,082		
	Speciality cakes			
101025	Appleford	35,025		
102025	Great Marcle	20,697		
103025	Norton	35,776		
104025	Wyvern	76,374		
	EXPENDITURE			
	Materials			
205055	Baking	247,291		
206055	Cake icing	29,843		
207055	Packaging	22,047		
208055	Administration/shop costs	12,976		
209055	Advertising	8,241		
	Labour			
205065	Baking	195,834		
206065	Cake icing	33,176		
207065	Packaging	42,958		
208065	Administration/shop costs	42,324		
209065	Advertising	29,722		
	Expenses			
205075	Baking	88,391		
206075	Cake icing	22,482		
207075	Packaging	30,056		
208075	Administration/shop costs	17,641		
209075	Advertising	35,024		

COST PERFORMANCE REPORT

May 2004

	Actual £ May 2004	Budget £ May 2004	Actual £ Year to date	Budget £ Year to date
MATERIALS		65,000		375,000
LABOUR		85,000		390,000
EXPENSES		47,000		250,000

COST DIFFERENCES (VARIANCES) REPORT

May 2004

	MONTH £	YEAR TO DATE £
MATERIALS		
LABOUR		
EXPENSES		

COMMENTS

SALES PERFORMANCE REPORT

May 2004

	Actual £ May 2004	Budget £ May 2004	Actual £ Year to date	Budget £ Year to date
APPLEFORD		56,000		364,000
GREAT MARCLE		33,000		195,000
NORTON		40,000		235,000
WYVERN		90,000		540,000

SALES DIFFERENCES (VARIANCES) REPORT

May 2004

	MONTH £	YEAR TO DATE £
APPLEFORD		
GREAT MARCLE		
NORTON		
WYVERN		

COMMENTS

INVOICE

JOHNSON PACKAGING LTD

6 Highfield Trading Estate Lampeter LL4 7YG
VAT Reg 235 6257 23

CODE: *20 50 65*

invoice to

Flour Pot Bakery Limited
61 Fore Street
Wyvern
WV1 3GH

invoice no	7724
account	246
your reference	377
date/tax point	25 05 04

product code	description	quantity	price	unit	total	discount	net
6667	Foodwrap film 750mm	100	4.50	roll	450.00	90.00	360.00

goods total	360.00
VAT	63.00
TOTAL	423.00

terms
Net 30 days

INVOICE

Wyvern Press

Windsor House, Hylton Road, Wyvern WV3 6BZ
VAT Reg 893 4572 12

CODE: *20 90 75*

invoice to

Flower Garden Designs
89 Fore Street
Wyvern
WV1 3GH

invoice no	2705
account	4226
your reference	390
date/tax point	24 05 04

product code	description	quantity	price	unit	total	discount	net
LP	Classified Advert	1	120.00	each	120.00	0.00	120.00

goods total	120.00
VAT	21.00
TOTAL	141.00

terms
Net 30 days

INVOICE

Confectionery Supplies Limited

29 Stockley Estate, Bristol, BS5 7FG
VAT Reg 462 3409 57

CODE: *20 60 55*

invoice to

Flour Pot Bakery Limited
61 Fore Street
Wyvern
WV1 3GH

invoice no	2721
account	5291
your reference	364
date/tax point	25 05 04

product code	description	quantity	price	unit	total	discount	net
FI67	Fondant icing ref67	10	12.00	packs	120.00	18.00	102.00

goods total	102.00
VAT	00.00
TOTAL	102.00

terms
Net 30 days

NOTE

to ______________________________

from ______________________________

date ______________________________

TELEPHONE MESSAGE

to Alex Wright

from Jade Simmons

date 1 June 2004 12.15

Emma Jones, Manager of the Norton shop 'phoned to say that a market research company was doing a survey of local shopping trends and wanted to know what the sales of our four shops were.
What should I tell her?
I said someone would phone her back this afternoon.
Thanks

Jade

what would you tell her?

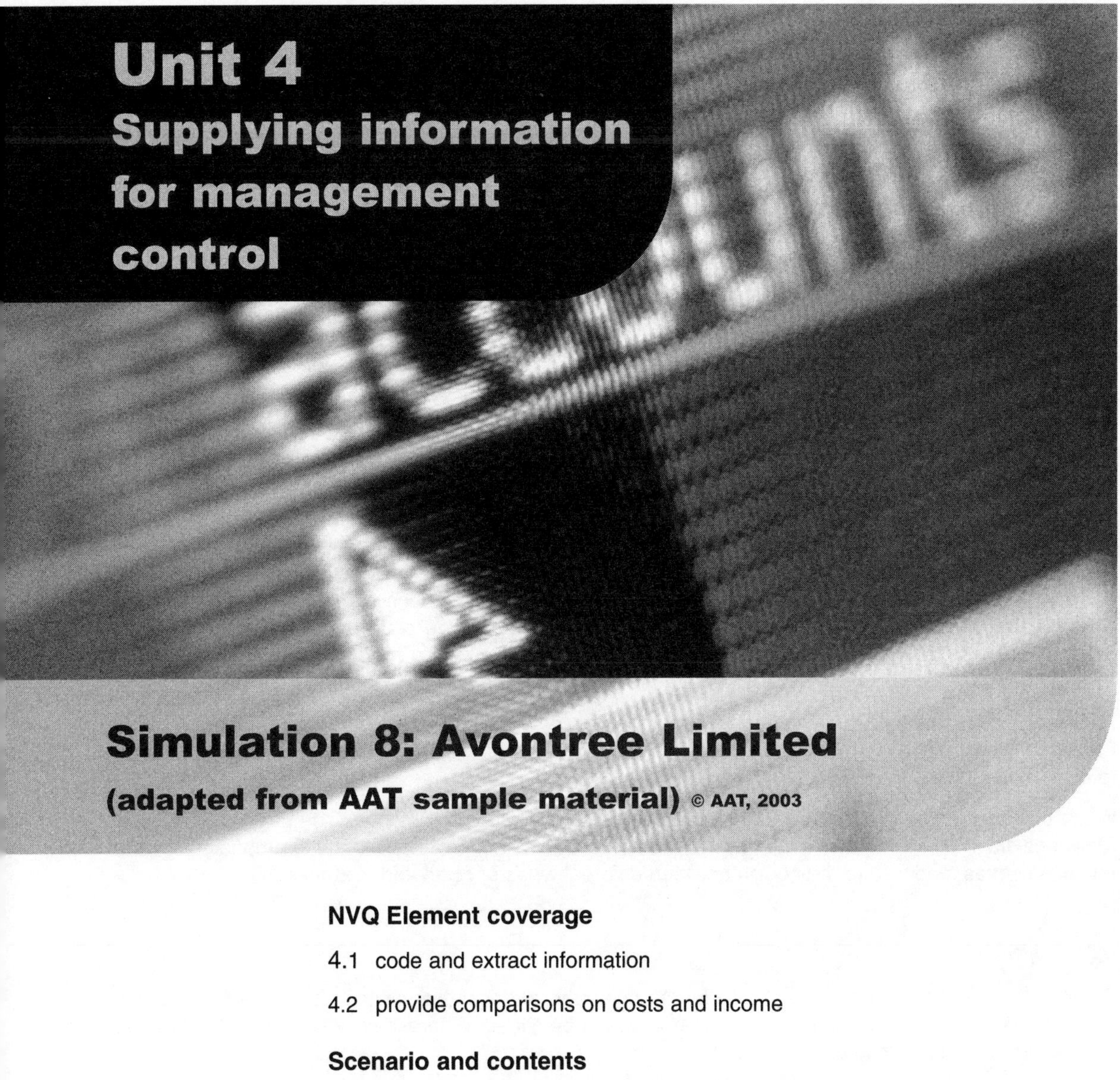

Unit 4 Supplying information for management control

Simulation 8: Avontree Limited

(adapted from AAT sample material)

NVQ Element coverage

4.1 code and extract information

4.2 provide comparisons on costs and income

Scenario and contents

This Simulation is based on Avontree Limited, a publisher of educational textbooks, which the company sells to schools and colleges. The tasks in the simulation involve providing financial information and reports to management. They include:

- the coding of sales figures, suppliers' invoices and payroll data
- checking coding on invoices and identifying errors
- a year-to-year comparison of year-to-date figures for sales and expenses
- calculating differences/variances between the year-to-date figures
- reporting differences/variances to a supervisor as appropriate

Suggested time allocation: three hours plus fifteen minutes reading time

SIMULATION 8
AVONTREE LIMITED

SITUATION

Your name is Parfraz Mehdi, and you are an Accounts Assistant working for Avontree Limited, Unit 5, Burberry Business Park, Newfields NF8 2PR. Avontree is a publisher of textbooks used in primary, secondary and higher education. You report to the Accounts Supervisor, Emily Padden.

CODING OF ORIGINAL DOCUMENTS

Avontree's accounts are maintained on a simple computerised system. One of your responsibilities is to code original documents for entry onto this system. For example, you code both sales and purchase invoices and enter relevant details onto data input sheets, which are then used for entering data into the computer system. In some cases you delegate the original coding to a colleague.

Payroll is maintained by Emily Padden on a computerised system separate from the accounts system. Each month she provides you with a payroll printout. Your task is to enter the appropriate codes for posting to the accounts system.

When doing your coding, you will need to refer to the company's policy manual; see pages 371-372 for relevant extracts. The purpose of the coding is to allocate costs and revenues to the appropriate cost and revenue centres, and also to distinguish between different types of costs and revenues.

VAT

Coding of VAT is performed automatically by the computerised accounts system, and therefore it is the amount *before* VAT on a purchase invoice that needs to be coded. There is no VAT on Avontree's sales invoices because textbooks are zero-rated.

DATES

In this simulation you will be dealing with transactions arising in May and June 2003.

Today's date is 9 June 2003.

TASKS

1 On pages 373-376 you will find eight sales invoices.

Enter relevant details of the sales invoices, including appropriate codes, on the data input sheet on page 383. You will need to refer to the extract from the company's policy manual on page 371.

2 On pages 377-382 you will find purchase invoices received from Avontree's suppliers, and related purchase orders raised by Avontree. The purchase invoices have already been coded by one of your colleagues.

Check the purchase invoices to ensure that they match the purchase orders, and also check that your colleague has entered the correct codes on the invoices. You will need to refer to the extract from the company's policy manual on page 372.

Your checks should reveal discrepancies. Draft an email to Emily Padden describing these discrepancies. Use the blank email on page 384.

3 The payroll printout for May 2003 is shown on page 382.

Enter the appropriate amounts and codes on the input sheet on page 385, ready for inputting the payroll details to the accounts system.

4 Refer to the report on page 385. This has been extracted from the accounts system and shows the year-to-date (YTD) totals for certain revenue and expenditure accounts up to the end of May 2003, along with comparative figures for the previous year.

In the column headed 'Variance £', enter the monetary amount of the variance (difference), between this year and last, using the symbol '+' to indicate an increase over last year and the symbol '–' to indicate a decrease compared with last year.

In the column headed 'Variance %', enter each variance (difference) as a percentage of last year's total, again using the symbols '+' and '–' and expressing the percentages to one decimal place.

To help you, the first line of the schedule has already been completed.

5 Draft a brief report to Emily Padden, to which you will attach the schedule you prepared in Task 4. Draw her attention to any instances where the calculated variance exceeds 5%. Use page 386 and date your report 9 June 2003.

DATA

COMPANY POLICY MANUAL (extracts)

Coding of sales revenue

Each item of sales revenue must be coded with two pieces of information:

- the revenue centre (see below)
- the type of revenue (see below)

The type of revenue is indicated by the product code. Textbooks for primary education have codes beginning with P. Textbooks for secondary education have codes beginning with S. Textbooks for higher education have codes beginning with H.

Only the net goods value is coded (i.e. the value of goods after deduction of trade discount).

Revenue centres

UK Sales	100
Overseas sales	200

Types of revenue

Textbook sales: primary education	300
Textbook sales: secondary education	400
Textbook sales: higher education	500

Coding of expenditure

Each item of expenditure must be coded with two pieces of information:

- the cost centre (see below)
- the type of expenditure (see below)

Cost centres

Typesetting costs	610
Editing costs	620
Printing and binding costs	630
Distribution and despatch costs	640
Marketing costs	650
Establishment costs	660

Types of cost

Materials	710
Expenses	720
Salaries	730

The cost of services performed by external individuals or organisations are classified as 'expenses'.

The costs of paying internal staff are classified as 'salaries'.

All salaries are classified to the 'establishment costs' cost centre.

CUSTOMER INVOICES

Please see pages 373-376.

SUPPLIER INVOICES

Please see pages 377-379.

SALES INVOICE
Avontree Limited
Unit 5, Burberry Business Park, Newfields NF8 2PR

Invoice to:
Megabooks Limited
33 High Street
Maidenhead SL6 1PQ
UK

VAT Registration: 225 6712 89
Date/tax point: 5 June 2003
Invoice number: 52711

Titles supplied	Item code	Quantity	List price (£)	Total (£)
GCSE Mathematics	S2251	10	12.50	125.00
Intermediate Mathematics	S1201	12	5.50	66.00
Total at list price				191.00
Less trade discount @ 35%				66.85
Net goods value				124.15
VAT @ 0%				0.00
Total due				124.15

Terms: net 30 days

SALES INVOICE
Avontree Limited
Unit 5, Burberry Business Park, Newfields NF8 2PR

Invoice to:
Books Plus
102 Lampard Avenue
Bristol BS3 5EW
UK

VAT Registration: 225 6712 89
Date/tax point: 5 June 2003
Invoice number: 52712

Titles supplied	Item code	Quantity	List price (£)	Total (£)
Applications of Electronics	H3141	4	27.00	108.00
Thermodynamics	H2278	2	32.50	65.00
Total at list price				173.00
Less trade discount @ 40%				69.20
Net goods value				103.80
VAT @ 0%				0.00
Total due				103.80

Terms: net 30 days

SALES INVOICE

Avontree Limited

Unit 5, Burberry Business Park, Newfields NF8 2PR

Invoice to:
Empstone Books Ltd
14 Cygnet Street
Holyport SO13 7KK
UK

VAT Registration: 225 6712 89
Date/tax point: 5 June 2003
Invoice number: 52713

Titles supplied	Item code	Quantity	List price (£)	Total (£)
The Metres of English Poetry	S1190	3	16.00	48.00
Tudor History for Teenagers	S3124	6	14.00	84.00
The Stuarts: a Brief Survey	S5155	6	14.00	84.00
Total at list price				216.00
Less trade discount @ 32.5%				70.20
Net goods value				145.80
VAT @ 0%				0.00
Total due				145.80

Terms: net 30 days

SALES INVOICE

Avontree Limited

Unit 5, Burberry Business Park, Newfields NF8 2PR

Invoice to:
Win Hong Books
17 Swire Street
Central
HONG KONG

VAT Registration: 225 6712 89
Date/tax point: 5 June 2003
Invoice number: 52714

Titles supplied	Item code	Quantity	List price (£)	Total (£)
Daily Life in Ancient Egypt	P9124	20	6.20	124.00
Daily Life in Ancient Rome	P9130	20	6.20	124.00
Total at list price				248.00
Less trade discount @ 35%				86.80
Net goods value				161.20
VAT @ 0%				0.00
Total due				161.20

Terms: net 30 days

SALES INVOICE
Avontree Limited
Unit 5, Burberry Business Park, Newfields NF8 2PR

Invoice to:
Tradesales Limited
65 Limetree Avenue
Birkenhead WA12 5TR
UK

VAT Registration: 225 6712 89
Date/tax point: 5 June 2003
Invoice number: 52715

Titles supplied	Item code	Quantity	List price (£)	Total (£)
GCSE Mathematics	S2251	4	12.50	50.00
A level Mathematics	S1452	10	15.00	150.00
Total at list price				200.00
Less trade discount @ 40%				80.00
Net goods value				120.00
VAT @ 0%				0.00
Total due				120.00

Terms: net 30 days

SALES INVOICE
Avontree Limited
Unit 5, Burberry Business Park, Newfields NF8 2PR

Invoice to:
Palmer and Company
18 Ambleden Avenue
Rystone
UK

VAT Registration: 225 6712 89
Date/tax point: 5 June 2003
Invoice number: 52716

Titles supplied	Item code	Quantity	List price (£)	Total (£)
GCSE French	S4123	20	12.80	256.00
GCSE Spanish	S4145	16	12.80	204.80
Total at list price				460.80
Less trade discount @ 35%				161.28
Net goods value				299.52
VAT @ 0%				0.00
Total due				299.52

Terms: net 30 days

SALES INVOICE
Avontree Limited
Unit 5, Burberry Business Park, Newfields NF8 2PR

Invoice to:
Business Books
18 High Street
Hensham CV28 5AP
UK

VAT Registration: 225 6712 89
Date/tax point: 5 June 2003
Invoice number: 52717

Titles supplied	Item code	Quantity	List price (£)	Total (£)
Management Principles and Practice	H3121	8	26.50	212.00
Total at list price				212.00
Less trade discount @ 30%				63.60
Net goods value				148.40
VAT @ 0%				0.00
Total due				148.40

Terms: net 30 days

SALES INVOICE
Avontree Limited
Unit 5, Burberry Business Park, Newfields NF8 2PR

Invoice to:
Megabooks Limited
33 High Street
Maidenhead SL6 1PQ
UK

VAT Registration: 225 6712 89
Date/tax point: 5 June 2003
Invoice number: 52718

Titles supplied	Item code	Quantity	List price (£)	Total (£)
En Avant: French for Beginners	S2234	22	16.00	352.00
Total at list price				352.00
Less trade discount @ 35%				123.20
Net goods value				228.80
VAT @ 0%				0.00
Total due				228.80

Terms: net 30 days

SALES INVOICE

The Boxshop

25 Lyme Street, Taunton, TA2 4RP

Invoice to:		
Avontree Limited	VAT Registration:	254 1781 26
Unit 5	Date/tax point:	5 June 2003
Burberry Business Park	Invoice number:	288712
Newfields NF8 2PR	Your order:	2305

Description of goods/services	Total (£)
2,000 postal despatch boxes, PDB126	765.00
Goods total	765.00
VAT @ 17.5%	133.87
Total due	**898.87**

Amount (£)	Cost centre/ revenue centre	Expenditure/ revenue type
765.00	640	710

Terms: net 30 days

SALES INVOICE

Editype Limited

28 Wakeland Road, Newfields NF4 7LK

Invoice to:		
Avontree Limited	VAT Registration:	267 9912 46
Unit 5	Date/tax point:	5 June 2003
Burberry Business Park	Invoice number:	2511
Newfields NF8 2PR		

Description of goods/services	Total (£)
Editorial work to your specification on *Corporate Strategy*	400.00
Total at list price	400.00
VAT @ 17.5%	70.00
Total due	**470.00**

Amount (£)	Cost centre/ revenue centre	Expenditure/ revenue type
400.00	620	720

Terms: net 30 days

SALES INVOICE

Education Magazine
17 Britton Street, London EC1M 5TP

Invoice to:
Avontree Limited
Unit 5
Burberry Business Park
Newfields NF8 2PR

VAT Registration:	315 8123 49
Date/tax point:	5 June 2003
Invoice number:	22111098
Your order:	2259

Description of goods/services	**Total (£)**
Sales advertisement in June 2003 issue	870.00

Amount (£)	Cost centre/ revenue centre	Expenditure/ revenue type
870.00	650	720

Total at list price	870.00
VAT @ 17.5%	152.25
Total due	1,022.25

Terms: net 30 days

SALES INVOICE

Litho Printing Limited
Rosina Street, London E8 7RT

Invoice to:
Avontree Limited
Unit 5
Burberry Business Park
Newfields NF8 2PR

VAT Registration:	412 5512 38
Date/tax point:	5 June 2003
Invoice number:	217765
Your order:	2271

Description of goods/services	**Total (£)**
Printing and binding 5,000 copies of *The War of the Roses*	16,410.00

Amount (£)	Cost centre/ revenue centre	Expenditure/ revenue type
16,410.00	630	710

Total at list price	16,410.00
VAT: zero-rated	0.00
Total due	**16,410.00**

Terms: net 30 days

SALES INVOICE

Typetext Limited

21 Ashton Lane, Newfields NF2 7UT

Invoice to:
Avontree Limited
Unit 5
Burberry Business Park
Newfields NF8 2PR

VAT Registration:	251 7171 34
Date/tax point:	5 June 2003
Invoice number:	276
Your order:	2286

Description of goods/services	Total (£)
Typesetting of *GCSE Geography* to agreed specification	1,200.00
Total at list price	1,200.00
VAT @ 17.5%	210.00
Total due	**1,410.00**

Amount (£)	Cost centre/ revenue centre	Expenditure/ revenue type
1,200.00	610	720

Terms: net 30 days

SALES INVOICE

Decofix Limited

Panton Close, Newfields NF8 2PR

Invoice to:
Avontree Limited
Unit 5
Burberry Business Park
Newfields NF8 2PR

VAT Registration:	381 5512 60
Date/tax point:	5 June 2003
Invoice number:	198
Your order:	2268

Description of goods/services	Total (£)
Repainting of accounts office to agreed specification	312.00
Total at list price	312.00
VAT @ 17.5%	54.60
Total due	**366.60**

Amount (£)	Cost centre/ revenue centre	Expenditure/ revenue type
312.00	660	710

Terms: net 30 days

PURCHASE ORDER
Avontree Limited
Unit 5, Burberry Business Park,
Newfields NF8 2PR

To:

Litho Printing Limited
Rosina Street
London E8 7RT

Date: 13 May 2003
Order no: 2271

Please supply the items/services below on the agreed terms.

Quantity	*Description*	*Item code*
500	Bound copies of The Wars of the Roses	N/A

On behalf of Avontree Limited: Emily Padden

PURCHASE ORDER
Avontree Limited
Unit 5, Burberry Business Park,
Newfields NF8 2PR

To:

The Boxshop
25 Lyme Street
Taunton TA2 4RP

Date: 20 May 2003
Order no: 2305

Please supply the items/services below on the agreed terms.

Quantity	*Description*	*Item code*
2,000	Postal despatch boxes	PDB126

On behalf of Avontree Limited: Emily Padden

PURCHASE ORDER
Avontree Limited
Unit 5, Burberry Business Park,
Newfields NF8 2PR

To:

Decofix Limited — Date: 12 May 2003

Panton Close — Order no: 2268

Newfields NF6 3QT

Please supply the items/services below on the agreed terms.

Quantity	*Description*	*Item code*
1	Repainting of accounts office as per quote dated 1 May 2003	N/A

On behalf of Avontree Limited: Emily Padden

PURCHASE ORDER
Avontree Limited
Unit 5, Burberry Business Park,
Newfields NF8 2PR

To:

Typestext Limited — Date: 16 May 2003

21 Ashton Lane — Order no: 2286

Newfields NF2 7UT

Please supply the items/services below on the agreed terms.

Quantity	*Description*	*Item code*
1	Typesetting of GCSE Geography – normal rates apply	N/A

On behalf of Avontree Limited: Emily Padden

PURCHASE ORDER
Avontree Limited
Unit 5, Burberry Business Park,
Newfields NF8 2PR

To:

Education Magazine
17 Britton Street
London EC1M 5TP

Date: 9 May 2003
Order no: 2259

Please supply the items/services below on the agreed terms.

Quantity	*Description*	*Item code*
1	Sales advertisement in June 2003 issue	N/A

On behalf of Avontree Limited: Emily Padden

SALARIES SUMMARY

Month: May 2003

Employee name	**Gross pay** (£)	**PAYE tax** (£)	**Employee** NIC (£)	**Net pay** (£)	**Employer** NIC (£)
James Bailey	850.00	91.00	46.60	712.40	54.99
Laura Drinkwater	3,000.00	572.00	215.00	2,213.00	308.57
Allan Holmes	1,250.00	189.00	86.60	974.40	102.19
Caroline Johnson	1,000.00	139.00	61.40	799.60	72.45
Parfraz Mehdi	1,400.00	225.00	101.40	1,073.60	119.65
Emily Padden	2,300.00	418.00	191.40	1,690.60	225.85
Roland White	1,100.00	157.00	71.40	871.60	84.25
	10,900.00	1,791.00	773.80	8,335.20	967.95

ANSWER PAGES

DATA INPUT SHEET

Sales Invoices **Date:**

		Coding		
Invoice Number	*Customer*	*Amount (£)*	*Revenue centre*	*Type of revenue*

EMAIL

from	Parfraz Mehdi
to	
cc	
subject	
date	9 June 2003

message

DATA INPUT SHEET – PAYROLL date ____________

	Coding		
Detail	*Amount £*	*Cost centre*	*Type of expenditure*

AVONTREE LIMITED

PROFIT AND LOSS ACCOUNT

Date: 31 May 2003

		Year-to-date			
Account code	Account name	This year	Last year	Variance £	Variance %
100-300	UK sales: primary	75,600	74,100	+1,500	+2.0
100-400	UK sales: secondary	100,900	108,700		
100-500	UK sales: higher	98,700	95,000		
610-720	Typesetting: expenses	15,300	16,000		
620-720	Editing: expenses	16,400	15,700		
630-710	Printing & binding: materials	40,100	36,500		
640-710	Distribution: materials	4,600	6,100		
650-720	Marketing: expenses	16,400	15,900		
660-720	Establishment: expenses	5,600	5,200		
660-730	Establishment: salaries	34,200	33,000		

REPORT

To:

From:

Subject:

Date:

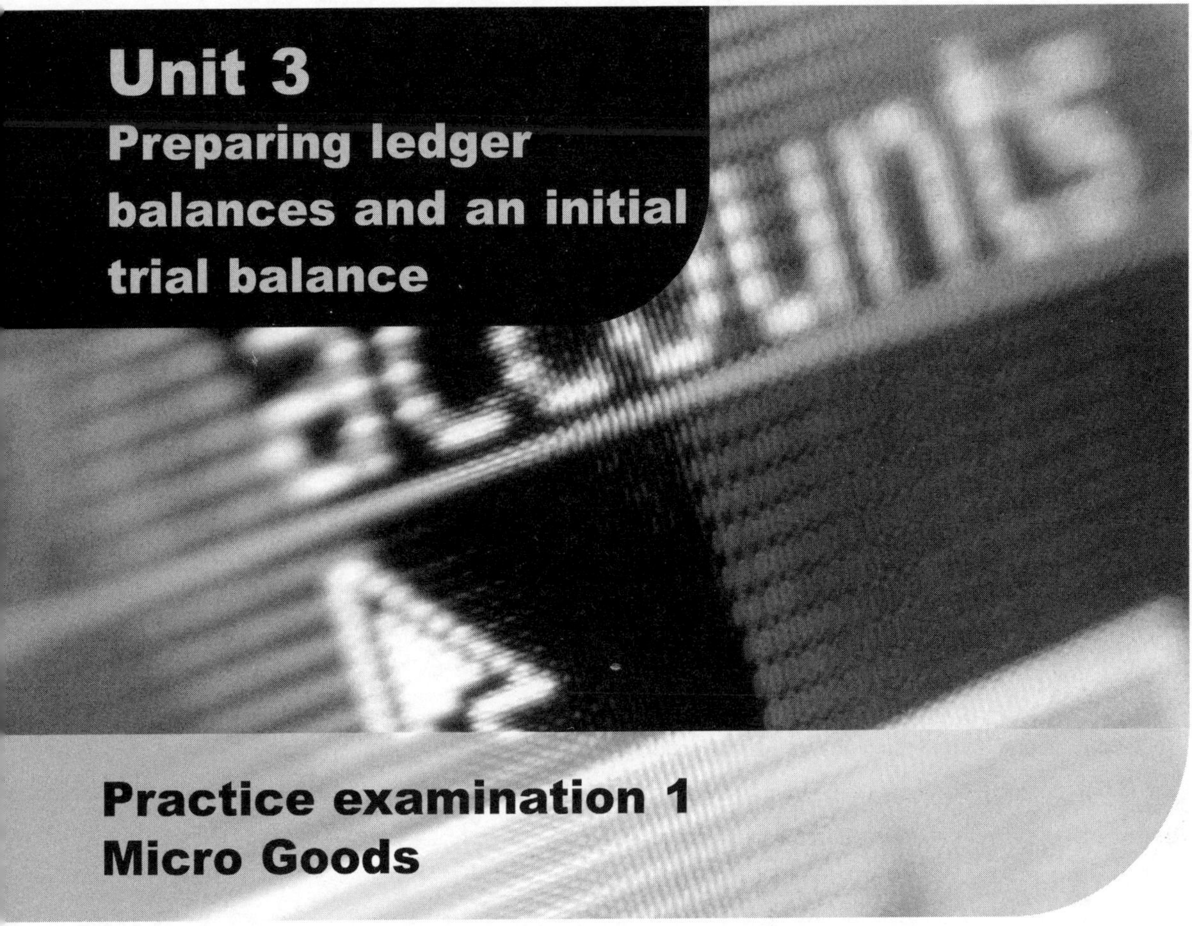

Unit 3
Preparing ledger balances and an initial trial balance

Practice examination 1
Micro Goods

NVQ Element coverage

3.1 balance bank transactions

3.2 prepare ledger balances and control accounts

3.3 draft an initial trial balance

Suggested time allocation

Three hours and fifteen minutes (to include a recommended fifteen minutes reading time).

PRACTICE EXAMINATION 1
MICRO GOODS

This Examination is in two sections.

You have to show competence in both sections, so attempt and aim to complete every task in both sections.

Section 1	Processing exercise
	Complete all six tasks
Section 2	10 tasks and questions
	Complete all tasks and questions

You should spend about 90 minutes on each section.

Include all essential workings within your answers, or use blank workings sheets, where appropriate.

Sections 1 and 2 both relate to the business described below.

INTRODUCTION

- Anna Lee is the owner of Micro Goods, a business that supplies the MG800 computer.
- You are employed by the business as a book-keeper.
- The business operates a manual accounting system.
- Double entry takes place in the Main (General) Ledger. Individual accounts of sales ledger and purchases ledger are kept in subsidiary ledgers as memorandum accounts.
- Assume today's date is 30 June 2004 unless otherwise instructed.

SECTION 1 – PROCESSING EXERCISE

You should spend about 90 minutes plus reading time answering this section.
Show your workings – use blank workings sheets.

DATA

Balances at the start of the day on 30 June 2004

The following balances are relevant to you at the start of the day on 30 June 2004:

	£
Credit suppliers	
PPP Limited	18,375
Jones and Bailey	2,800
Pickford Parts	10,050
Butler and Hart	6,410
Purchases	299,600
Purchases returns	1,360
Purchases ledger control	126,760
Loan from bank	3,000
Discounts received	200
Insurance	540
Motor tax	180
VAT (credit balance)	18,643

Task 1.1

Enter these opening balances into the following accounts, given on pages 392-395.

Subsidiary (Purchases) Ledger

PPP Limited
Jones and Bailey
Pickford Parts
Butler and Hart

Main (General) Ledger

Purchases
Purchases returns
Purchases ledger control
Loan from bank
Discounts received
Insurance
Motor tax
VAT

Note: The lines shown in the accounts on pages 392-395 are there to help you present your work neatly and clearly. You may not need to use all of the lines.

DATA

TRANSACTIONS

The following transactions all took place on 30 June 2004 and have been entered into the relevant books of prime entry as shown below. No entries have yet been made into the ledger system. The VAT rate is 17.5%.

Purchases day book

Date 2004	Details	Invoice Number	Total £	VAT £	Net £
30 June	PPP Limited	6931	2,350	350	2,000
30 June	Jones and Bailey	30001	9,400	1,400	8,000
30 June	Pickford Parts	P300	7,050	1,050	6,000
30 June	Butler and Hart	4821	47	7	40
	Totals		18,847	2,807	16,040

Purchases returns day book

Date 2004	Details	Credit Note No	Total £	VAT £	Net £
30 June	PPP Limited	CR0116	329	49	280
30 June	Pickford Parts	CR119	5,875	875	5,000
	Totals		6,204	924	5,280

Cash book

Date 2004	Details	Discounts allowed £	Bank £	Date 2004	Details	Discounts received £	Bank £
30 June	Balance b/f		6,320	30 June	Loan repayment		280
				30 June	Insurance		830
				30 June	Motor tax		90
				30 June	PPP Limited (creditor)	30	2,000
				30 June	Balance c/f		3,120
	Totals		6,320			30	6,320

Task 1.2

From the day books and cash book shown above, make the relevant entries into the accounts in the Subsidiary (Purchases) Ledger, and Main (General) Ledger.

Task 1.3

Balance the accounts showing clearly the balances *carried down* at 30 June (closing balance).

Task 1.4

Now that you have closed the accounts for June, prepare the accounts for the coming month by showing clearly the balance brought down at 1 July (opening balance).

SUBSIDIARY (PURCHASES) LEDGER

PPP Limited

Date	*Details*	*Amount* £	*Date*	*Details*	*Amount* £

Jones and Bailey

Date	*Details*	*Amount* £	*Date*	*Details*	*Amount* £

Pickford Parts

Date	*Details*	*Amount* £	*Date*	*Details*	*Amount* £

Butler and Hart

Date	*Details*	*Amount* £	*Date*	*Details*	*Amount* £

MAIN (GENERAL) LEDGER

Purchases

Date	*Details*	*Amount* £	*Date*	*Details*	*Amount* £

Purchases returns

Date	*Details*	*Amount* £	*Date*	*Details*	*Amount* £

Purchases ledger control

Date	Details	Amount £	Date	Details	Amount £

Loan from bank

Date	Details	Amount £	Date	Details	Amount £

Discounts received

Date	Details	Amount £	Date	Details	Amount £

Insurance

Date	*Details*	*Amount* £	*Date*	*Details*	*Amount* £

Motor tax

Date	*Details*	*Amount* £	*Date*	*Details*	*Amount* £

VAT

Date	*Details*	*Amount* £	*Date*	*Details*	*Amount* £

DATA

Other balances to be transferred to the trial balance:

	£
Motor vehicles	16,400
Office equipment	28,000
Stock	21,500
Cash	480
Sales ledger control	201,910
Capital	2,245
Sales	460,172
Sales returns	1,500
Discounts allowed	600
Wages	28,000
Rates	1,400
Heat and light	2,042
Telephone	608
Motor fuel	1,800
Miscellaneous expenses	1,500

Task 1.5

Transfer the balances that you calculated in task 1.3, and the bank balance, to the trial balance on page 397.

Task 1.6

Transfer the remaining balances shown above to the trial balance on page 397, and total each column.

Trial Balance as at 30 June 2004

	Debit (£)	Credit (£)
Motor vehicles	....	....
Office equipment	....	....
Stock	....	....
Bank	....	....
Cash	....	....
Sales ledger control	....	....
Purchases ledger control	....	....
VAT	....	....
Capital	....	....
Sales	....	....
Sales returns	....	....
Purchases	....	....
Purchases returns	....	....
Discounts allowed	....	....
Loan from bank	....	....
Discounts received	....	....
Wages	....	....
Insurance	....	....
Motor tax	....	....
Rates	....	....
Heat and light	....	....
Telephone	....	....
Motor fuel	....	....
Miscellaneous expenses	....	....
Total	....	....

SECTION 2 – TASKS AND QUESTIONS

You should spend about 90 minutes plus reading time on this section.
Answer all of the following questions on pages 398-406. Write your answers in the space provided.

Task 2.1

Micro Goods have the following cash and cheques to bank on 30 June:

Cash		*Cheques*	
One	£20 note	B Bradley Limited	£100.00
Twelve	£10 notes	C McGregor	£15.50
Fifteen	£2 coins	G Grove	£200.00
Eight	50p coins		

Complete both sides of the paying-in slip below.

Date_______________ **bank giro credit**

Cashier's stamp

Southern Bank plc
Southampton

Account
MICRO GOODS
BUSINESS ACCOUNT
Paid in by/Ref

NO. OF CHEQUES

40-23-76	31176802	78

Notes £50		
Notes £20		
Notes £10		
Notes £5		
£2		
£1		
50p		
20p		
10p, 5p		
2p, 1p		
Total Cash		
Cheques, POs		
£		

Please do not write or mark below this line or fold this voucher

II000000II 40II2376II 31176802II 78

Cheques etc.

£			brought forward £		
carried forward £			carried forward £		

Task 2.2

Although Micro Goods normally banks a customer's cheque on the day it is received, it cannot make withdrawals against that cheque for a few days.

Briefly give the reason for this delay.

. . . .

. . . .

. . . .

. . . .

Task 2.3

The bank current account balance in the trial balance can be on the debit side or credit side depending on whether the business has money in the bank or an overdraft.

Name ONE other account in the trial balance which can normally have either a debit or a credit balance.

. . . .

Task 2.4

A purchases invoice has been incorrectly calculated by the supplier and the incorrect total entered in the accounting records of Micro Goods. (Ignore VAT.)

(a) Would this cause an imbalance in the trial balance?

Yes / No (circle your answer)

(b) Briefly give the reason for your answer.

. . . .

. . . .

. . . .

. . . .

Task 2.5

Micro Goods has agreed to buy a second hand motor car for £6,000 for business use. The seller does not want to accept a business cheque, in case it is dishonoured, and he does not want cash.

(a) What service offered by banks would you recommend to Micro Goods?

....

(b) What would be the bookkeeping entries required in the Main (General) Ledger to record the purchase?

Debit ....

Credit ....

Task 2.6

Anna Lee would like to computerise the accounting records and payroll. However, she is worried that all employees who use the computers would have access to confidential accounting and payroll information.

(a) Give ONE control within a computerised system which would overcome this problem.

....

....

....

(b) What type of computerised system would link the accounting and payroll programmes together?

....

Task 2.7

Anna Lee insists that each account in the Main (General) Ledger is balanced at the end of each month, and the balance brought down is clearly shown.

Give ONE problem which you, as the bookkeeper, would face if the balances were not clearly identified at the end of each month.

....

....

Task 2.8

The following errors have been made in the Main (General) Ledger of Micro Goods:

(a) £85 has been debited to the insurance account instead of the motor tax account.

(b) Purchases valued at £7,000 have been credited to the purchases account and debited to the purchases ledger control account (ignore VAT).

(c) A credit customer, T G Boon Limited, has ceased trading. The amount outstanding on its account of £250 plus VAT has been written off in the Subsidiary (Sales) Ledger only, but the net amount and VAT should also have been written off as a bad debt.

Record the journal entries necessary in the Main (General) Ledger to correct the above. Narratives are not required.

Note: You do NOT need to adjust accounts in Section 1.

JOURNAL			
Date	Details	Dr £	Cr £

Task 2.9

The following is a summary of transactions with credit customers in June:

	£
Credit sales	118,600
Money received from credit customers	96,214
Discounts allowed	300
Sales returns from credit customers	650
Bad debt written off	350

The balance of debtors at 1 June 2004 was £180,824.

(a) Prepare a sales ledger control account from the above details, showing clearly the balance carried down.

Sales ledger control

Date	*Details*	*Amount* £	*Date*	*Details*	*Amount* £

Task 2.9 continued

The following balances were shown in the subsidiary (sales) ledger on 30 June:

	£	
Carless and Company	76,560	debit
BBT Limited	28,109	debit
Dale and Company	32,019	debit
Vale Computers	1,645	debit
Brandon Limited	350	debit
Bissell and Bradley	31,304	debit
Hopkins and Company	32,273	debit

(b) Reconcile these balances with the sales ledger control account balance you calculated on page 402.

	£
Sales ledger control account balance as at 30 June 2004	....
Total of subsidiary (sales) ledger accounts as at 30 June 2004	....
Difference	....

(c) What do you think may have caused the difference calculated in (b)?

....

....

....

....

Task 2.10

On 2 July Micro Goods received its bank statement as at 30 June 2004, shown below.

(a) Check the items on the bank statement against the items in the cash book.

(b) Update the cash book as needed.

(c) Total the cash book and clearly show the balance carried down.

Note: You do not need to adjust accounts in Section 1.

Southern Bank plc
High Street, Southampton, SO12 1BD

To: Micro Goods **Account No: 31176802** **30 June 2004**

STATEMENT OF ACCOUNT

Date	Details	Paid out	Paid in	Balance
2004		£	£	£
1 June	Balance b/f			8,196C
5 June	Cheque No 816078	800		7,396C
5 June	Credit		2,000	9,396C
8 June	BACS Credit L Candy		3,500	12,896C
11 June	Cheque No 816079	1,864		11,032C
15 June	Direct Debit A L Jones Limited	700		10,332C
20 June	Bank charges	52		10,280C
25 June	Direct Debit CCC Properties	400		9,880C
29 June	Cheque No 816081	1,290		8,590C

D = Debit C = Credit

Task 2.10 continued

CASH BOOK

Date 2004	Details	Bank £	Date 2004	Cheque No	Details	Bank £
1 June	Balance b/f	7,396	1 June	816079	Instone Institute	1,864
5 June	C Crown	2,000	5 June	816080	Long and Lowe	2,120
29 June	B Rudge	5,120	22 June	816081	Albert Rowe	1,290
			29 June	816082	AMC Limited	7,400
			29 June	816083	B Price	200

(d) Using the information on pages 404 and 405, prepare a bank reconciliation statement (see next page) as at 30 June. The bank reconciliation statement should start with the balance as per the bank statement and reconcile to the balance as per the cash book.

Task 2.10 continued

Bank reconciliation statement as at 30 June 2004

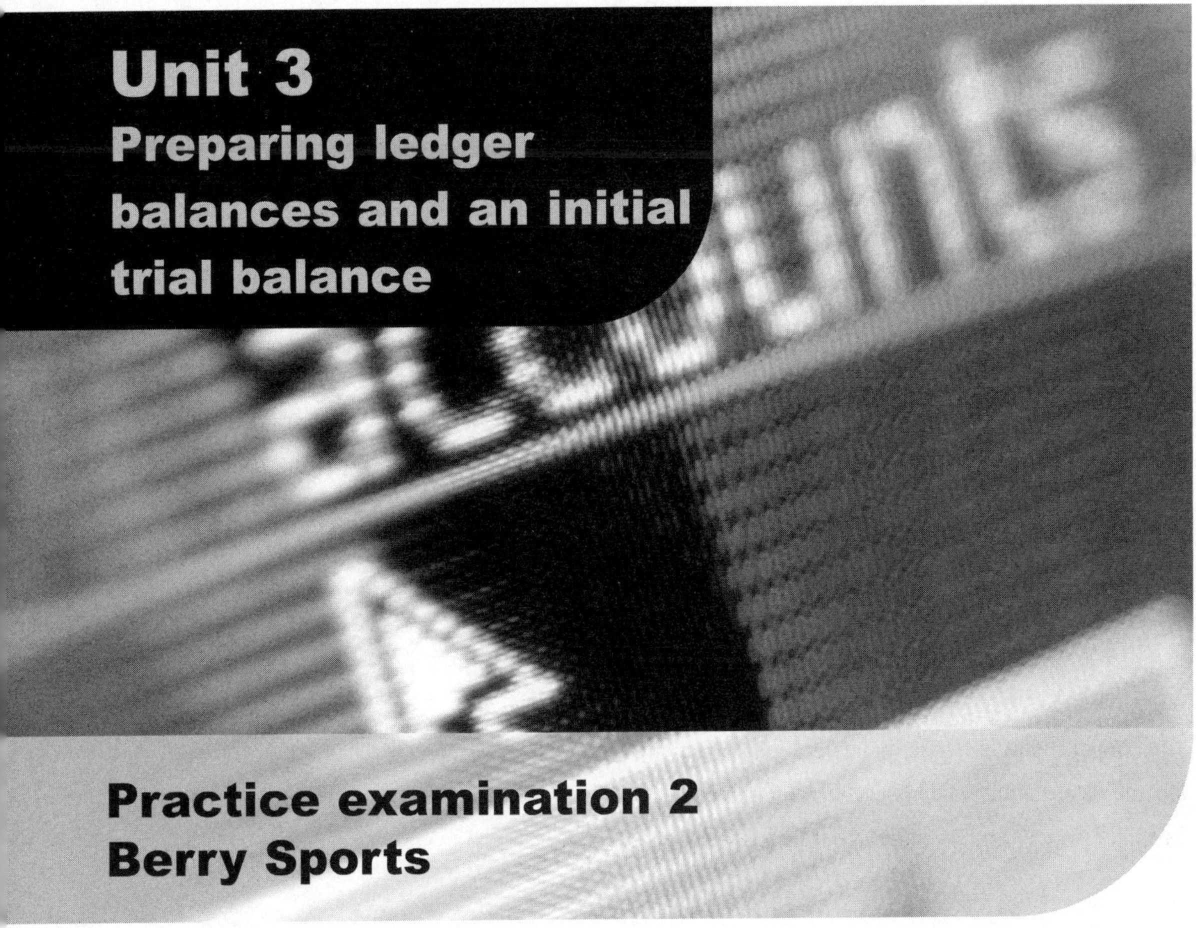

Unit 3
Preparing ledger balances and an initial trial balance

Practice examination 2
Berry Sports

NVQ Element coverage

3.1 balance bank transactions

3.2 prepare ledger balances and control accounts

3.3 draft an initial trial balance

Suggested time allocation

Three hours and fifteen minutes (to include a recommended fifteen minutes reading time).

PRACTICE EXAMINATION 2
BERRY SPORTS

This Examination is in two sections.

You have to show competence in both sections, so attempt and aim to complete every task in both sections.

Section 1	Processing exercise
	Complete all six tasks
Section 2	10 tasks and questions
	Complete all tasks and questions

You should spend about 90 minutes on each section.

Include all essential workings within your answers, or use blank workings sheets, where appropriate.

Sections 1 and 2 both relate to the business described below.

INTRODUCTION

- John Berry is the owner of Berry Sports, a business that supplies sportswear.
- You are employed by the business as a book-keeper.
- The business operates a manual accounting system.
- Double entry takes place in the Main (General) Ledger. Individual accounts of sales ledger and purchases ledger are kept in subsidiary ledgers as memorandum accounts.
- Assume today's date is 30 November 2004 unless otherwise instructed.

SECTION 1 - PROCESSING EXERCISE

You should spend about 90 minutes plus reading time answering this section.
Show your workings – use blank workings sheets.

DATA

Balances at the start of the day on 30 November 2004

The following balances are relevant to you at the start of the day on 30 November 2004:

	£
Credit customers	
Jay and Company	24,000
Central Gym	15,671
BBT Limited	24,156
Leisure Unlimited	12,387
Sales	609,102
Sales returns	2,100
Sales ledger control	156,922
Loan from bank	5,000
Discounts allowed	500
Rent payable	10,693
Heat and light	2,765
VAT (credit balance)	17,585

Task 1.1

Enter these opening balances into the following accounts given on pages 411-414:

Subsidiary (Sales) Ledger

- Jay and Company
- Central Gym
- BBT Limited
- Leisure Unlimited

Main (General) Ledger

- Sales
- Sales returns
- Sales ledger control
- Loan from bank
- Discounts allowed
- Rent payable
- Heat and light
- VAT

Note: The lines shown in the accounts on pages 411-414 are there to help you present your work neatly and clearly. You may not need to use all of the lines.

DATA

TRANSACTIONS

The following transactions all took place on 30 November 2004 and have been entered into the relevant books of prime entry as shown below. No entries have yet been made into the ledger system. The VAT rate is 17.5%.

Sales day book

Date 2004	Details	Invoice No	Total £	VAT £	Net £
30 Nov	Jay and Company	2010	3,525	525	3,000
30 Nov	Central Gym	2011	8,225	1,225	7,000
30 Nov	BBT Limited	2012	1,175	175	1,000
30 Nov	Leisure Unlimited	2013	9,635	1,435	8,200
	Totals		22,560	3,360	19,200

Sales returns day book

Date 2004	Details	Credit Note No	Total £	VAT £	Net £
30 Nov	BBT Limited	CR220	470	70	400
30 Nov	Leisure Unlimited	CR221	2,350	350	2,000
	Totals		2,820	420	2,400

Cash book

Date 2004	Details	Discounts allowed £	Bank £	Date 2004	Details	Discounts received £	Bank £
30 Nov	Balance b/f		1,650	30 Nov	Loan repayment		600
30 Nov	Jay and Co	50	4,000	30 Nov	Rent		1,300
				30 Nov	Heat and light		350
				30 Nov	Balance c/f		3,400
	Totals	50	5,650				5,650

Task 1.2 From the day books and cash book shown above, make the relevant entries into the accounts in the Subsidiary (Sales) Ledger and Main (General) Ledger.

Task 1.3 Balance the accounts showing clearly the balances *carried down* at 30 November (closing balance).

Task 1.4 Now that you have closed the accounts for November, prepare the accounts for the coming month by showing clearly the balances *brought down* at 1 December (opening balance).

SUBSIDIARY (SALES) LEDGER

Jay and Company

Date	Details	Amount £	Date	Details	Amount £

Central Gym

Date	Details	Amount £	Date	Details	Amount £

BBT Limited

Date	Details	Amount £	Date	Details	Amount £

Leisure Unlimited

Date	Details	Amount £	Date	Details	Amount £

MAIN (GENERAL) LEDGER

Sales

Date	Details	Amount £	Date	Details	Amount £

Sales returns

Date	Details	Amount £	Date	Details	Amount £

Sales ledger control

Date	Details	Amount £	Date	Details	Amount £

Loan from bank

Date	Details	Amount £	Date	Details	Amount £

Discounts allowed

Date	Details	Amount £	Date	Details	Amount £

Rent payable

Date	*Details*	*Amount* £	*Date*	*Details*	*Amount* £

Heat and light

Date	*Details*	*Amount* £	*Date*	*Details*	*Amount* £

VAT

Date	*Details*	*Amount* £	*Date*	*Details*	*Amount* £

DATA

Other balances to be transferred to the trial balance:

	£
Motor vehicles	35,800
Office equipment	16,750
Stock	10,957
Cash	900
Purchases ledger control	50,226
Capital	5,541
Purchases	395,189
Purchases returns	1,820
Discounts received	1,200
Wages	46,000
Insurance	3,000
Rates	2,550
Telephone	1,298
Motor expenses	2,400
Miscellaneous expenses	1,000

Task 1.5

Transfer the balances that you calculated in task 1.3, and the bank balance, to the trial balance on page 416.

Task 1.6

Transfer the remaining balances shown above to the trial balance on page 416, and total each column.

Trial Balance as at 30 November 2004

	Debit £	Credit £
Motor vehicles	....	....
Office equipment	....	....
Stock	....	....
Bank	....	....
Cash	....	....
Sales ledger control	....	....
Purchases ledger control	....	....
VAT	....	....
Capital	....	....
Sales	....	....
Sales returns	....	....
Purchases	....	....
Purchases returns	....	....
Discounts allowed	....	....
Loan from bank	....	....
Discounts received	....	....
Wages	....	....
Insurance	....	....
Rent payable	....	....
Rates	....	....
Heat and light	....	....
Telephone	....	....
Motor expenses	....	....
Miscellaneous expenses	....	....
Total	....	....

SECTION 2 – TASKS AND QUESTIONS

You should spend about 90 minutes plus reading time on this section.

Answer all of the following questions on pages 417-424.

Write your answers in the space provided.

Note: accounts in the Subsidiary (Sales) Ledger and Main (General) Ledger do not need to be adjusted as a result of the work you do in this section.

Task 2.1

The following three credit card sale transactions have taken place today at Berry Sports.

Credit card transaction 1	£830.00
Credit card transaction 2	£600.00
Credit card transaction 3	£75.00

Complete the bank summary voucher in respect of these transactions.

	£	p
1		
2		
3		
4		
5		
6		
7		
8		
9		
10		
11		
12		
13		
14		
15		
16		
17		
18		
19		
20		
Total		Carried overleaf

DO NOT TICK OR MAKE ANY MARKS OUTSIDE THE LISTING AREA

HAVE YOU IMPRINTED THE SUMMARY WITH YOUR RETAILER'S CARD?

BANK Processing (White) copy of Summary with your Vouchers in correct order.

1. SUMMARY
2. SALES VOUCHERS
3. REFUND VOUCHERS

KEEP Retailer's copies (Blue &Yellow)

DO NOT USE Staples, Pins, Paper Clips

	ITEMS	AMOUNT	
SALES VOUCHERS (LISTED OVERLEAF)			
LESS REFUND VOUCHERS			
DATE	TOTAL		

SUMMARY - RETAILER'S COPY

BANKING SUMMARY

RETAILER'S SIGNATURE

Task 2.2

Berry Sports is planning to buy new office furniture and has agreed to pay the supplier by 12 monthly payments of £100.

Which method of payment offered by banks would be the most appropriate?

....

Task 2.3

The subsidiary (sales) ledger shows the amounts owed by *individual* debtors; the sales ledger control account shows the *total* amount owed by debtors.

Give TWO reasons for maintaining a sales ledger control account.

....

....

....

Task 2.4

Berry Sports keeps a *petty cash control account* in the main (general) ledger and the petty cash book is the subsidiary account. In November £56 was spent from petty cash and at the end of the month £100 was put into the petty cash box from the bank.

(a) Enter these transactions into the petty cash control account below, showing clearly the balance carried down.

Petty cash control					
Date	Details	Amount	Date	Details	Amount
2004		£	2004		£
1 Nov	Balance b/f	100			

(b) Name ONE other check you would carry out to ensure the petty cash book is correct.

....

....

....

Task 2.5

John Berry is considering computerising the accounting system.

Name ONE advantage to Berry Sports of a computerised accounting system.

....

....

....

Task 2.6

Berry Sports incurs costs which would be described as *revenue expenditure* such as wages, rent, rates, electricity.

Name TWO items of *capital expenditure* that Berry Sports may incur.

....

....

....

Task 2.7

All documents sent out and received by Berry Sports are filed alphabetically.

Suggest ONE alternative way of filing each of the following documents, giving a different method for each.

(a) Sales invoices ....

(b) Purchases invoices ....

(c) Contracts ....

Task 2.8

The following errors have been made in the accounting records of Berry Sports:

(a) £110 has been debited to the rent account instead of the rates account.

(b) Purchases returns valued at £300 have been debited to the purchases returns account and credited to the purchases ledger control account.

(c) £2,000 has been debited to the insurance account and credited to the bank account instead of the correct amount of £200.

Record the journal entries necessary in the Main (General) Ledger to correct the above. Narratives are not required.

JOURNAL

Date	Details	Dr £	Cr £

Task 2.9

The purchases ledger control account has a credit balance of £50,226 as at 30 November 2004.

Confirm the accuracy of this figure by completing the document below using the following information:

	£
Balance of creditors control account as at 1 November 2004	49,167
Purchases invoices received in November	7,219
Purchases credit notes received in November	600
Payments made in November	5,200
Discounts received in November	360

Purchases ledger control account check as at 30 November 2004

	£	£
Balance as at 1 November 2004		....
Purchases invoices received	....	
Purchases credit notes received	....	
Payments made to creditors	....	
Discounts received	....	....
Balance as at 30 November 2004		....

Task 2.10

On 2 December Berry Sports received a bank statement as at 30 November 2004.

(a) Check the items on the bank statement (below) against the items in the cash book (on the next page).

(b) Update the cash book as needed.

(c) Total the cash book and clearly show the balance carried down.

MIDWAY BANK PLC

To: Berry Sports **Account No: 45619822** **30 November 2004**

STATEMENT OF ACCOUNT

Date	Details	Paid out	Paid in	Balance
2004		£	£	£
1 Nov	Balance b/f			9,000C
5 Nov	Cheque No 625109	6,300		2,700C
5 Nov	Credit		10,000	12,700C
8 Nov	BACS Credit			
	B Green		3,500	16,200C
11 Nov	Cheque No 625110	1,100		15,100C
15 Nov	Direct Debit			
	LBO Limited	1,300		13,800C
20 Nov	Bank charges	29		13,771C
25 Nov	Direct Debit			
	HB Services	1,800		11,971C

D = Debit C = Credit

Task 2.10 continued

CASH BOOK

Date 2004	Details	Bank £	Date 2004	Cheque No	Details	Bank £
1 Nov	Balance b/f	9,000	1 Nov	625109	R B Lawley	6,300
5 Nov	L Burger	10,000	5 Nov	625110	B&B Limited	1,100
22 Nov	D Smith	1,396	22 Nov	625111	M Parkes	300
			22 Nov	625112	Richards Limited	9,667

(d) Using the information on pages 422 and 423, prepare a bank reconciliation statement (see next page) as at 30 November. The bank reconciliation statement should start with the balance as per the bank statement and reconcile to the balance as per the cash book.

Task 2.10 continued

Bank reconciliation statement as at 30 November 2004

Unit 3
Preparing ledger balances and an initial trial balance

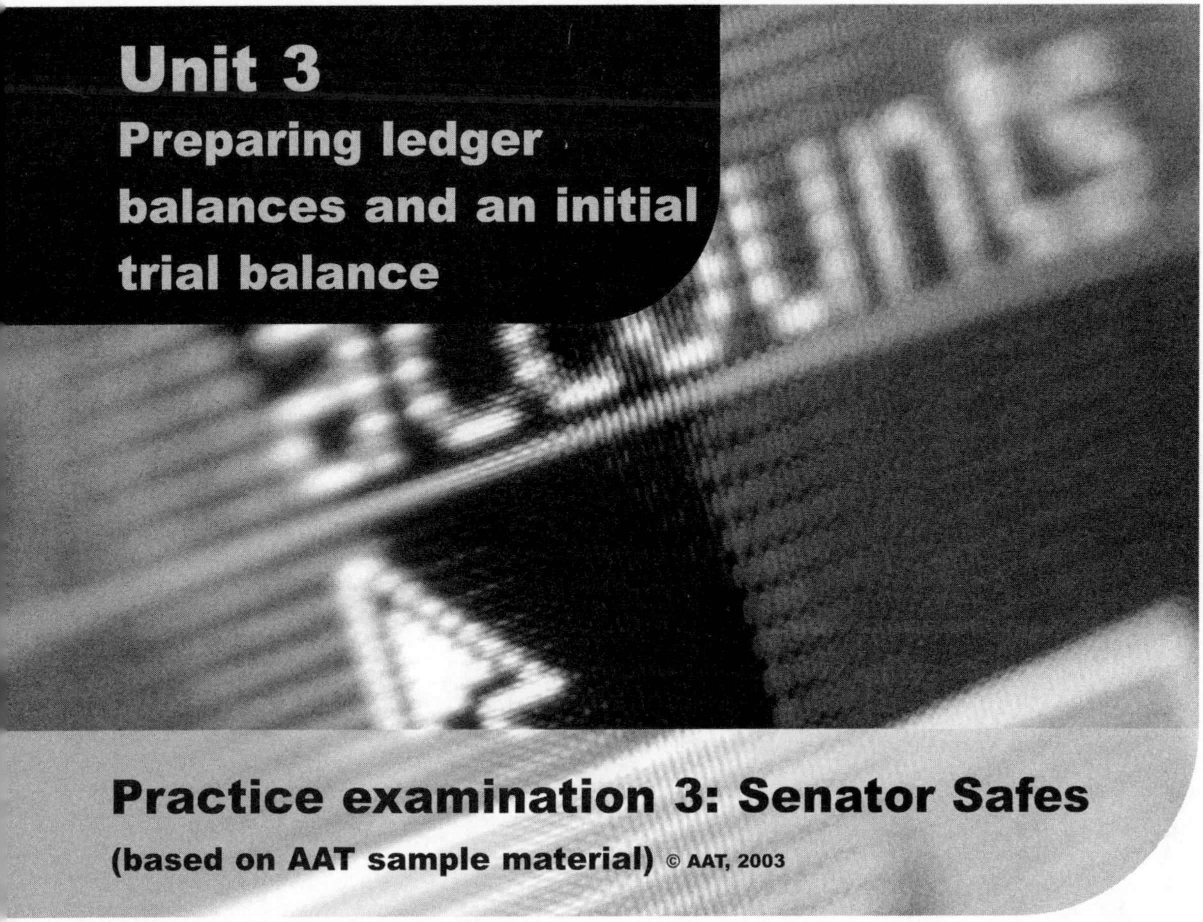

Practice examination 3: Senator Safes

(based on AAT sample material)

NVQ Element coverage

3.1 balance bank transactions

3.2 prepare ledger balances and control accounts

3.3 draft an initial trial balance

Suggested time allocation

Three hours and fifteen minutes (to include a recommended fifteen minutes reading time).

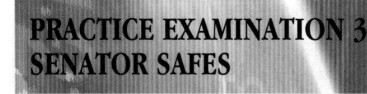

PRACTICE EXAMINATION 3
SENATOR SAFES

This Examination is in two sections.

You have to show competence in both sections, so attempt and aim to complete every task in both sections.

Section 1	Processing exercise
	Complete all six tasks
Section 2	10 tasks and questions
	Complete all tasks and questions

You should spend about 90 minutes on each section.

Include all essential workings within your answers, or use blank workings sheets, where appropriate.

Sections 1 and 2 both relate to the business described below.

INTRODUCTION

- Karen Davies is the owner of Senator Safes, a business that supplies fireproof safes.
- You are employed by the business as a book-keeper.
- The business uses a manual accounting system.
- Double entry takes place in the Main (General) Ledger. Individual accounts of debtors and creditors are kept in subsidiary ledgers as memorandum accounts.
- Assume today's date is 30 June 2004 unless you are told otherwise.

SECTION 1 – PROCESSING EXERCISE

You should spend about 90 minutes plus reading time answering this section.
Show your workings – use blank workings sheets.

DATA

Balances at the start of the day on 30 June 2004

The following balances are relevant to you at the start of the day on 30 June 2004.

	£
Trade debtors	
JPD Limited	15,873
Lewis and Lane	25,109
Barker and Company	2,192
Higgins Limited	10,354
Sales	573,012
Sales returns	1,200
Sales ledger control	134,100
Loan from bank	6,500
Discounts allowed	870
Rent	5,350
Motor expenses	2,760
VAT (credit balance)	15,400

Task 1.1

Enter these opening balances into the following accounts, given on pages 429-432.

Subsidiary (Sales) Ledger

- JPD Limited
- Lewis and Lane
- Barker and Company
- Higgins Limited

Main (General) Ledger

- Sales
- Sales returns
- Debtors control
- Loan from bank
- Discounts allowed
- Rent
- Motor expenses
- VAT

Note: The lines shown in the accounts on pages 429-432 are there to help you present your work neatly and clearly. You may not need to use all of the lines.

DATA

TRANSACTIONS

The following transactions all took place on 30 June 2004 and have been entered into the relevant books of prime entry as shown below. No entries have yet been made into the ledger system. The VAT rate is 17.5%.

Sales day book

Date 2004	Details	Invoice Number	Total £	VAT £	Net £
30 June	JPD Limited	1216	2,350	350	2,000
30 June	Lewis and Lane	1217	9,400	1,400	8,000
30 June	Barker and Company	1218	1,880	280	1,600
30 June	Higgins Limited	1219	3,525	525	3,000
	Totals		17,155	2,555	14,600

Sales returns day book

Date 2004	Details	Credit Note Number	Total £	VAT £	Net £
30 June	Barker and Company	CR30	4,230	630	3,600
30 June	Higgins Limited	CR31	1,410	210	1,200
	Totals		5,640	840	4,800

Cash book

Date 2004	Details	Discounts allowed £	Bank £	Date 2004	Details	Discounts received £	Bank £
30 June	Balance b/f		9,036	30 June	Loan repayment		500
30 June	JPD Limited	35	2,100	30 June	Rent		1,000
30 June	Higgins Limited		200	30 June	Motor expenses		180
				30 June	Balance c/f		9,656
	Totals	35	11,336				11,336

Task 1.2 From the day books and cash book shown above, make the relevant entries into the accounts in the Subsidiary (Sales) Ledger and Main (General) Ledger.

Task 1.3 Balance the accounts showing clearly the balances *carried down* at 30 June (closing balance).

Task 1.4 Now that you have closed the accounts for June, prepare the accounts for the coming month by showing clearly the balances *brought down* at 1 July (opening balance).

SUBSIDIARY (SALES) LEDGER

JPD Limited

Date	*Details*	*Amount* £	*Date*	*Details*	*Amount* £

Lewis and Lane

Date	*Details*	*Amount* £	*Date*	*Details*	*Amount* £

Barker and Company

Date	*Details*	*Amount* £	*Date*	*Details*	*Amount* £

Higgins Limited

Date	*Details*	*Amount* £	*Date*	*Details*	*Amount* £

MAIN (GENERAL) LEDGER

Sales

Date	*Details*	*Amount* £	*Date*	*Details*	*Amount* £

Sales returns

Date	*Details*	*Amount* £	*Date*	*Details*	*Amount* £

Sales ledger control

Date	*Details*	*Amount* £	*Date*	*Details*	*Amount* £

Loan from bank

Date	*Details*	*Amount* £	*Date*	*Details*	*Amount* £

Discounts allowed

Date	*Details*	*Amount* £	*Date*	*Details*	*Amount* £

Rent

Date	Details	Amount £	Date	Details	Amount £

Motor expenses

Date	Details	Amount £	Date	Details	Amount £

VAT

Date	Details	Amount £	Date	Details	Amount £

DATA

Other balances to be transferred to the trial balance:

	£
Motor vehicles	36,100
Office equipment	18,350
Stock	25,000
Cash	150
Purchases ledger control	32,060
Capital	9,600
Purchases	346,012
Purchases returns	3,600
Discounts received	2,000
Wages	38,249
Insurance	1,600
Rates	6,800
Telephone	1,845
Heat and light	2,100
Miscellaneous expenses	12,650

Task 1.5 Transfer the balances that you calculated in task 1.3, and the bank balance, to the trial balance on page 434.

Task 1.6 Transfer the remaining balances shown above to the trial balance on page 434, and total each column.

Trial Balance as at 30 June 2004

	Debit	Credit
	£	£
Motor vehicles	....	....
Office equipment	....	....
Stock	....	....
Bank	....	....
Cash	....	....
Sales ledger control	....	....
Purchases ledger control	....	....
VAT	....	....
Capital	....	....
Sales	....	....
Sales returns	....	....
Purchases	....	....
Purchases returns	....	....
Discounts allowed	....	....
Loan from bank	....	....
Discounts received	....	....
Wages	....	....
Insurance	....	....
Rent	....	....
Rates	....	....
Motor expenses	....	....
Telephone	....	....
Heat and light	....	....
Miscellaneous expenses	....	....
Total	....	....

SECTION 2 – TASKS AND QUESTIONS

You should spend about 90 minutes plus reading time on this section.

Answer all of the following questions on pages 435-444.

Write your answers in the space provided.

Task 2.1

The cheque below has been received today.

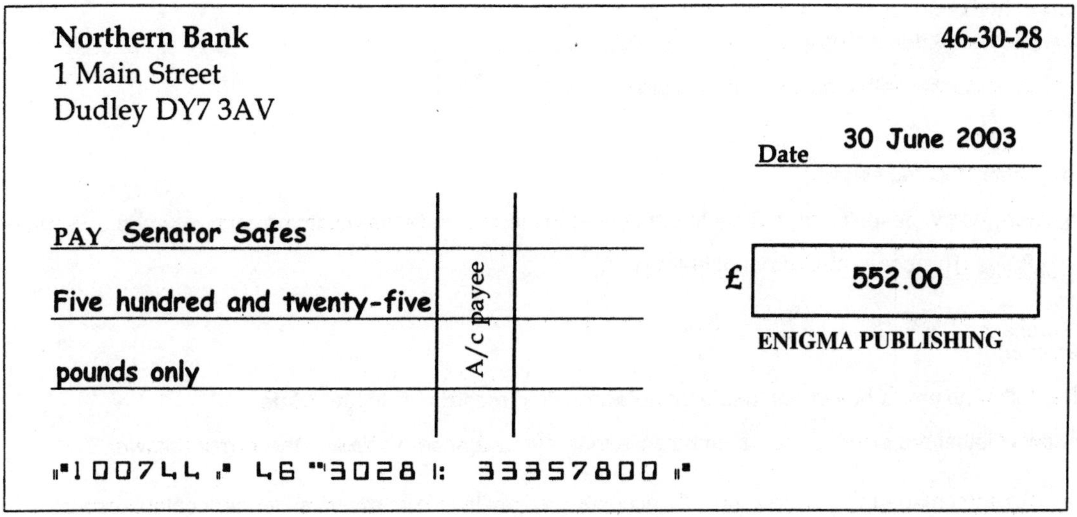
Northern Bank
1 Main Street
Dudley DY7 3AV

46-30-28

Date 30 June 2003

PAY Senator Safes

Five hundred and twenty-five pounds only

A/c payee

£ 552.00

ENIGMA PUBLISHING

100744 46 3028 33357800

(a) Give THREE reasons why the cheque will not be honoured (accepted) by the bank.

. . . .

. . . .

. . . .

(b) What is the branch sort code number on the cheque?

. . . .

Task 2.2

Complete the following sentences by writing the name of the appropriate document.

(a) Senator Safes sends a ....

to each customer at the end of every month to show how much is outstanding and to request a payment.

(b) Senator Safes sends a ....

to a customer to correct an overcharge on an invoice.

(c) Senator Safes sends a ....

to a supplier with a payment by cheque.

(d) Senator Safes sends a ....

with goods despatched to a customer. One copy is signed by the customer and returned to Senator Safes. This copy is the proof of delivery.

Task 2.3

The following errors have been made in the accounting records of Senator Safes.

Show whether the errors cause an imbalance in the trial balance by circling the correct answer.

(a) An entry made to the sales and VAT accounts but omitted from the sales ledger control account.

The trial balance will balance. / The trial balance will not balance.

(b) Omission of a purchase invoice from all accounting records.

The trial balance will balance. / The trial balance will not balance.

(c) VAT on an invoice incorrectly calculated.

The trial balance will balance. / The trial balance will not balance.

(d) An invoice entered in the account of B Fox instead of C Fox.

The trial balance will balance. / The trial balance will not balance.

Task 2.4

Karen Davies insists that all accounting records and source documents are locked away whenever the office is left unattended.

Give TWO reasons why it is important to do this.

. . . .

. . . .

. . . .

. . . .

Task 2.5

A cheque was received from a customer, L Brown, for £400 plus VAT. The cheque was entered in the cash book and ledgers. The bank then dishonoured the cheque.

(a) What bookkeeping entries would you need to make in the Main (General) Ledger to record the dishonoured cheque?

Dr ______________________________ £ __________

Cr ______________________________ £ __________

(b) Name TWO methods of payment Senator Safes could insist on which would avoid this happening again.

. . . .

. . . .

Task 2.6

Karen Davies is thinking about using a computerised accounting system. The automatic calculation of totals and balances will save time.

Name TWO other features of a computerised accounting system that will save time.

. . . .

. . . .

. . . .

. . . .

Task 2.7

Senator Safes operates a petty cash imprest system. The imprest amount is £200.00 and is restored on the first day of each month.

At the end of the month the following amounts had been spent:

Tea and coffee	£12.00
Stationery	£21.15
Travel	£60.00
Window cleaning	£30.00

(a) How much cash is required to restore the imprest level?

....

(b) How much will be in the petty cash tin on 1 July?

....

Task 2.8

The following errors have been made in the Main (General) Ledger of Senator Safes.

(a) An amount of £50 was debited to the suspense account. The following two errors have now been discovered:

- a figure in the sales account has been overstated by £75
- a figure in the insurance account has been overstated by £25

(b) Purchases returns have been entered in the accounting records as £706 instead of the correct amount of £607. (Ignore VAT.)

(c) A credit customer, Leeson and Company, has ceased trading. The amount outstanding on its account of £800 plus VAT has been written off as a bad debt in the Subsidiary (Sales) Ledger only, but the net amount and VAT should also have been written off.

Record the journal entries above in the Main (General) Ledger to correct the errors shown above. Narratives are not required.

Note: You do NOT need to adjust the accounts in Section 1.

JOURNAL

Date	Details	Dr £	Cr £

Task 2.9

The following entries were recorded in the Subsidiary (Purchases) Ledger during the month of June.

	£
Balance of creditors at 1 June 2004	50,300
Goods purchased on credit	21,587
Paid creditors	13,750
Discounts received	500
Goods returned to suppliers	250

(a) Prepare a purchases ledger control account from the above details. Show clearly the balance carried down at 30 June 2004.

Purchases ledger control

Date	Details	Amount £	Date	Details	Amount £

The following balances were in subsidiary (purchases) ledger on 30 June.

Wright and Company	£12,000	credit
CCY Limited	£11,107	credit
Carter and Company	£9,380	credit
Tomkins Limited	£16,800	credit
PP Properties	£500	debit
L Vakas	£1,200	credit
Ten Traders	£6,400	credit

(b) Reconcile the balances shown above with the purchases ledger control account balance you have calculated in part (a) on page 440.

	£
Purchases ledger control account balance as at 30 June 2004	....
Total of subsidiary (purchases) ledger accounts as at 30 June 2004	....
Difference	....

(c) What may have caused the difference you calculated in part (b) above?

....

....

....

Task 2.10

On 28 June Senator Safes received the following bank statement as at 24 June 2004.

SOUTH BANK PLC

High Street, Webley, W36 OKW

To: Senator Safes **Account No: 721982716** **24 June 2004**

STATEMENT OF ACCOUNT

Date	Details	Paid out	Paid in	Balance
2004		£	£	£
3 June	Balance b/f			7,000C
5 June	Cheque No 326705	300		6,700C
5 June	Cheque No 326710	6,900		200D
5 June	Cheque No 326711	300		500D
10 June	BACS Credit			
	C Maguire		9,100	8,600C
11 June	Cheque No 326713	76		8,524C
14 June	Direct Debit			
	Bamber Limited	1,300		7,224C
20 June	Direct Debit			
	Webley MBC	100		7,124C
24 June	Bank charges	52		7,072C

D = Debit C = Credit

The cash book as at 28 June 2004 is shown below.

Cash book

Date 2004	Details	Bank £	Date 2004	Cheque No	Details	Bank £
1 June	Balance b/f	6,700	1 June	326710	B Groom Limited	6,900
26 June	P Kramer	3,100	1 June	326711	KKD Limited	300
26 June	L Jones	82	6 June	326712	F Bolton	250
			7 June	326713	Leigh & Company	76

(a) Check the items on the bank statement against the items in the cash book.

(b) Update the cash book as needed.

(c) Total the cash book and clearly show the balance carried down.

Note: You do not need to adjust the accounts in Section 1.

(d) Using the information on pages 442 and 443, prepare a bank reconciliation statement as at 28 June. The bank reconciliation statement should start with the balance as per the bank statement and reconcile to the balance as per the cash book.

Bank reconciliation statement as at 28 June 2004

	£	£

Appendix

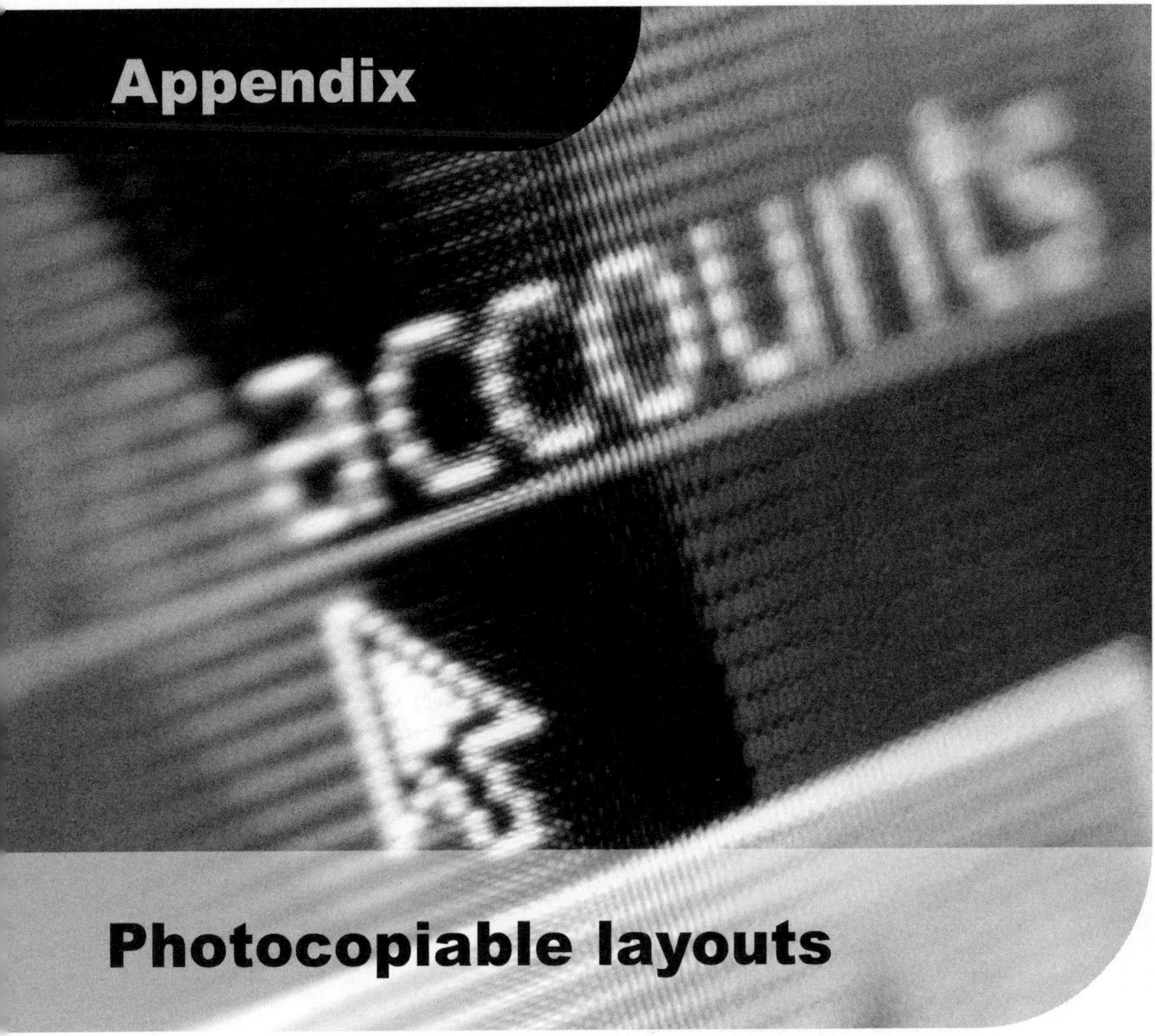

Photocopiable layouts

This appendix of photocopiable material comprises the following blank layouts:

- double-entry ledger accounts (page 446)
- sales day book (page 447)
- purchases day book (page 447)
- petty cash book (page 448)

You are free to photocopy these pages for classroom use, but they remain the copyright of the publisher and authors.

These layouts and a variety of financial documents are available for free download from our website: www.osbornebooks.co.uk

Dr Cr

Date	Details	Amount	Date	Details	Amount
		£			£

Dr Cr

Date	Details	Amount	Date	Details	Amount
		£			£

Dr Cr

Date	Details	Amount	Date	Details	Amount
		£			£